PRIMARY

Problem-solving in mathematics

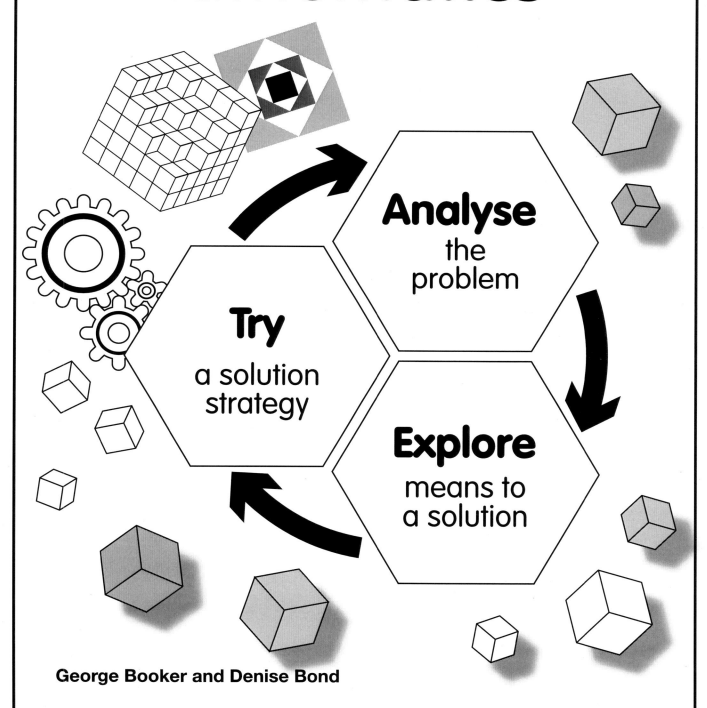

Analyse the problem

Try a solution strategy

Explore means to a solution

George Booker and Denise Bond

6036UK

Problem-solving in mathematics
(Book G)

Published by R.I.C. Publications® 2008

Republished under licence by Prim-Ed Publishing 2009

Copyright© George Booker and Denise Bond 2008

ISBN 978-1-84654-188-9

PR–6036

Titles available in this series:

Problem-solving in mathematics *(Book A)*
Problem-solving in mathematics *(Book B)*
Problem-solving in mathematics *(Book C)*
Problem-solving in mathematics *(Book D)*
Problem-solving in mathematics *(Book E)*
Problem-solving in mathematics *(Book F)*
Problem-solving in mathematics *(Book G)*

Internet websites

In some cases, websites or specific URLs may be recommended. While these are checked and rechecked at the time of publication, the publisher has no control over any subsequent changes which may be made to webpages. It is *strongly* recommended that the class teacher checks *all* URLs before allowing pupils to access them.

View all pages online

Website: www.prim-ed.com

Books A–G of ***Problem-solving in mathematics*** have been developed to provide a rich resource for teachers of pupils from the early years to the end of primary school and into secondary school. The series of problems, discussions of ways to understand what is being asked and means of obtaining solutions have been built up to improve the problem-solving performance and persistence of all pupils. It is a fundamental belief of the authors that it is critical that pupils and teachers engage with a few complex problems over an extended period rather than spend a short time on many straightforward 'problems' or exercises. In particular, it is essential to allow pupils time to review and discuss what is required in the problem-solving process before moving to another and different problem. This book includes extensive ideas for extending problems and solution strategies to assist teachers in implementing this vital aspect of mathematics in their classrooms. Also, the problems have been constructed and selected over many years' experience with pupils at all levels of mathematical talent and persistence, as well as in discussions with teachers in classrooms, professional learning and university settings.

Problem-solving does not come easily to most people, so learners need many experiences engaging with problems if they are to develop this crucial ability. As they grapple with problem, meaning and find solutions, pupils will learn a great deal about mathematics and mathematical reasoning; for instance, how to organise information to uncover meanings and allow connections among the various facets of a problem to become more apparent, leading to a focus on organising what needs to be done rather than simply looking to apply one or more strategies. In turn, this extended thinking will help pupils make informed choices about events that impact on their lives and to interpret and respond to the decisions made by others at school, in everyday life and in further study.

Pupil and teacher pages

The pupil pages present problems chosen with a particular problem-solving focus and draw on a range of mathematical understandings and processes. For each set of related problems, teacher notes and discussion are provided, as well as indications of how particular problems can be examined and solved. Answers to the more straightforward problems and detailed solutions to the more complex problems

ensure appropriate explanations. The use of the pages foster discussion among pupils and suggest ways in which problems can be extended. Related problems occur on one or more pages that extend the problem's ideas, the solution processes and pupils' understanding of the range of ways to come to terms with what problems are asking.

At the top of each teacher page, there is a statement that highlights the particular thinking that the problems will demand, together with an indication of the mathematics that might be needed and a list of materials that could be used in seeking a solution. A particular focus for the page or set of three pages of problems then expands on these aspects. Each book is organised so that when a problem requires complicated strategic thinking, two or three problems occur on one page (supported by a teacher page with detailed discussion) to encourage pupils to find a solution together with a range of means that can be followed. More often, problems are grouped as a series of three interrelated pages where the level of complexity gradually increases, while the associated teacher page examines one or two of the problems in depth and highlights how the other problems might be solved in a similar manner.

Each teacher page concludes with two further aspects critical to successful teaching of problem-solving. A section on likely difficulties points to reasoning and content inadequacies that experience has shown may well impede pupils' success. In this way, teachers can be on the look out for difficulties and be prepared to guide pupils past these potential pitfalls. The final section suggests extensions to the problems to enable teachers to provide several related experiences with problems of these kinds in order to build a rich array of experiences with particular solution methods; for example, the numbers, shapes or measurements in the original problems might change but leave the means to a solution essentially the same, or the context may change while the numbers, shapes or measurements remain the same. Then numbers, shapes or measurements and the context could be changed to see how the pupils handle situations that appear different but are essentially the same as those already met and solved. Other suggestions ask pupils to make and pose their own problems, investigate and present background to the problems or topics to the class, or consider solutions at a more general level (possibly involving verbal descriptions and eventually pictorial or symbolic arguments). In this way, not only are pupils' ways of thinking extended but the problems written on one page are used to produce several more problems that utilise the same approach.

Mathematics and language

The difficulty of the mathematics gradually increases over the series, largely in line with what is taught at the various year levels, although problem-solving both challenges at the point of the mathematics that is being learned as well as provides insights and motivation for what might be learned next. For example, the computation required gradually builds from additive thinking, using addition and subtraction separately and together, to multiplicative thinking, where multiplication and division are connected conceptions. More complex interactions of these operations build up over the series as the operations are used to both come to terms with problems' meanings and to achieve solutions. Similarly, two-dimensional geometry is used at first but extended to more complex uses over the range of problems, then joined by interaction with three-dimensional ideas. Measurement, including chance and data, also extends over the series from length to perimeter, and from area to surface area and volume, drawing on the relationships among these concepts to organise solutions as well as giving an understanding of the metric system. Time concepts range from interpreting timetables using 12-hour and 24-hour clocks while investigations related to mass rely on both the concept itself and practical measurements.

The language in which the problems are expressed is relatively straightforward, although this too increases in complexity and length of expression across the books in terms of both the context in which the problems are set and the mathematical content that is required. It will always be a challenge for some pupils to 'unpack' the meaning from a worded problem, particularly as problems' context, information and meanings expand. This ability is fundamental to the nature of mathematical problem-solving and needs to be built up with time and experiences rather than be diminished or left out of the problems' situations. One reason for the suggestion that pupils work in groups is to allow them to share and assist each other with the tasks of discerning meanings and ways to tackle the ideas in complex problems through discussion, rather than simply leaping into the first ideas that come to mind (leaving the full extent of the problem unrealised).

An approach to solving problems

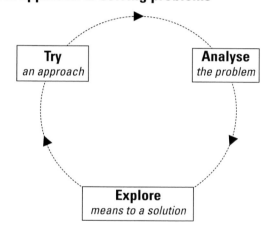

The careful, gradual development of an ability to analyse problems for meaning, organising information to make it meaningful and to make the connections among them more meaningful in order to suggest a way forward to a solution is fundamental to the approach taken with this series, from the first book to the last. At first, materials are used explicitly to aid these meanings and connections; however, in time they give way to diagrams, tables and symbols as understanding and experience of solving complex, engaging problems increases. As the problem forms expand, the range of methods to solve problems is carefully extended, not only to allow pupils to successfully solve the many

types of problems, but also to give them a repertoire of solution processes that they can consider and draw on when new situations are encountered. In turn, this allows them to explore one or other of these approaches to see whether each might furnish a likely result. In this way, when they try a particular method to solve a new problem, experience and analysis of the particular situation assists them to develop a full solution.

Not only is this model for the problem-solving process helpful in solving problems, it also provides a basis for pupils to discuss their progress and solutions and determine whether or not they have fully answered a question. At the same time, it guides teacher questions of pupils and provides a means of seeing underlying mathematical difficulties and ways in which problems can be adapted to suit particular needs and extensions. Above all, it provides a common framework for discussions between a teacher and group or whole class to focus on the problem-solving process rather than simply on the solution of particular problems. Indeed, as Alan Schoenfeld, in Steen L (Ed) *Mathematics and democracy* (2001), states so well, in problem-solving:

getting the answer is only the beginning rather than the end … an ability to communicate thinking is equally important.

We wish all teachers and pupils who use these books success in fostering engagement with problem-solving and building a greater capacity to come to terms with and solve mathematical problems at all levels.

George Booker and Denise Bond

CONTENTS

Problem-solving and mathematical thinking

By learning problem-solving in mathematics, pupils should acquire ways of thinking, habits of persistence and curiosity, and confidence in unfamiliar situations that will serve them well outside the mathematics classroom. In everyday life and in the workplace, being a good problem solver can lead to great advantages.

NCTM principles and standards for school mathematics (2000, p. 52)

Problem-solving lies at the heart of mathematics. New mathematical concepts and processes have always grown out of problem situations and pupils' problem-solving capabilities develop from the very beginning of mathematics learning. A need to solve a problem can motivate pupils to acquire new ways of thinking as well as to come to terms with concepts and processes that might not have been adequately learned when first introduced. Even those who can calculate efficiently and accurately are ill prepared for a world where new and adaptable ways of thinking are essential if they are unable to identify which information or processes are needed.

On the other hand, pupils who can analyse problem meanings, explore means to a solution and carry out a plan to solve mathematical problems have acquired deeper and more useful knowledge than simply being able to complete calculations, name shapes, use formulas to make measurements or determine measures of chance and data. It is critical that mathematics teaching focuses on enabling all pupils to become both able and willing to engage with and solve mathematical problems.

Well-chosen problems encourage deeper exploration of mathematical ideas, build persistence and highlight the need to understand thinking strategies, properties and relationships. They also reveal the central role of *sense making* in mathematical thinking—not only to evaluate the need for assessing the reasonableness of an answer or solution, but also the need to consider the inter-relationships among the information provided with a problem situation. This may take the form of number sense, allowing numbers to be represented in various ways and operations to be interconnected; through spatial sense that allows the visualisation of a problem in both its parts and whole; to a sense of measurement across length, area, volume and chance and data.

Problem-solving

A problem is a task or situation for which there is no immediate or obvious solution, so that *problem-solving* refers to the processes used when engaging with this task. When problem-solving, pupils engage with situations for which a solution strategy is not immediately obvious, drawing on their understanding of concepts and processes they have already met, and will often develop new understandings and ways of thinking as they move towards a solution. It follows that a task that is a problem for one pupil may not be a problem for another and that a situation that is a problem at one level will only be an exercise or routine application of a known means to a solution at a later time.

A large number of tourists visited Uluru during 2007. There were twice as many visitors in 2007 than in 2003 and 6530 more visitors in 2007 than in 2006. If there were 298 460 visitors in 2003, how many were there in 2006?

For a pupil aged 8-11 years, sorting out the information to see how the number of visitors each year are linked is a considerable task. There is also the need to use multiplication and subtraction with large numbers. For a pupil in later primary years, an ability to see how the problem is structured and familiarity with computation could lead them to use a calculator, key in the numbers and operation in an appropriate order and readily obtain the answer:

$$298460 \times 2 - 6530 = 590390$$
590 390 tourists visited Uluru in 2006

As the world in which we live becomes ever more complex, the level of mathematical thinking and problem-solving needed in life and in the workplace has increased considerably. Those who understand and can use the mathematics they have learned will have opportunities opened to them that those who do not develop these ways of thinking will not. To enable pupils to thrive in this changing world, attitudes and ways of knowing that enable them to deal with new or unfamiliar tasks are now as essential as the procedures that have always been used to handle familiar operations readily and efficiently. Such an attitude needs to develop from the beginning of mathematics learning as pupils form beliefs about meaning, the notion of taking control over the activities they engage with and the results they obtain, and as they build an inclination to try different approaches. In other words, pupils need to see mathematics as a way of thinking rather than a means of providing answers to be judged right or wrong by a teacher, textbook or some other external authority. They need to be led to focus on means of solving problems rather than on particular answers so that they understand the need to determine the meaning of a problem before beginning to work on a solution.

Lindsay sold 170 eggs at two different markets. She noticed that the number she sold at the second market was 10 less than half the number she sold at the first market. How many eggs did she sell at each market?

In order to solve this problem, it is not enough to simply use the numbers that are given. Rather, an analysis of the situation is needed first to see how the number sold at the second market relates to the number sold at the first market and the 170 eggs sold altogether. Putting the information onto a diagram can help:

First market		Second market
Half number sold at first market	Half number sold at first market	10 less than half number sold at first market

The sum of the numbers in the three sections of the diagram is 170; half + half + (half − 10) = 170, so 3 x half = 180. A diagram or use of materials are needed first to interpret the situation and then see how a solution can be obtained.

However, many pupils feel inadequate when they encounter problem-solving questions. They seem to have no idea of how to go about finding a solution and are unable to draw on the competencies they have learned in number, space and measurement. Often these difficulties stem from underdeveloped concepts for the operations, spatial thinking and measurement processes. They may also involve an underdeveloped capacity to read problems for meaning and a tendency to be led astray by the wording or numbers in a problem situation. Their approach may then simply be to try a series of guesses or calculations rather than consider using a diagram or materials to come to terms with what the problem is asking and using a systematic approach to organise the information given and required in the task. It is this ability to analyse problems that is the key to problem-solving, enabling decisions to be made about which mathematical processes to use, which information is needed and which ways of proceeding are likely to lead to a solution.

Making sense in mathematics

Making sense of the mathematics being developed and used needs to be seen as the central concern of learning. This is important, not only in coming to terms with problems and means to solutions, but also in terms of putting meanings, representations and relationships in mathematical ideas to the forefront of

viii
Problem-solving in mathematics
www.prim-ed.com   Prim-Ed Publishing®

thinking about and dealing with mathematics. Making sensible interpretations of any results and determining which of several possibilities is more or equally likely is critical in problem-solving.

Number sense, which involves being able to work with numbers comfortably and competently, is important in many aspects of problem-solving, in making judgments, interpreting information and communicating ways of thinking. It is based on a full understanding of numeration concepts such as zero, place value and the renaming of numbers in equivalent forms, so that 207 can be seen as 20 tens and 7 ones as well as 2 hundreds and 7 ones (or that $\frac{5}{2}$, 2.5 and $2\frac{1}{2}$ are all names for the same fraction amount). Automatic, accurate access to basic facts also underpins number sense, not as an end in itself, but rather as a means of combining with numeration concepts to allow manageable mental strategies and fluent processes for larger numbers. Well-understood concepts for the operations are essential in allowing relationships within a problem to be revealed and taken into account when framing a solution.

Number sense requires:
- understanding relationships among numbers
- appreciating the relative size of numbers
- a capacity to calculate and estimate mentally
- fluent processes for larger numbers and adaptive use of calculators
- an inclination to use understanding and facility with numeration and computation in flexible ways.

The following problem highlights the importance of these understandings.

There were 317 people at the New Year's Eve party on 31 December. If each table could seat 5 couples, how many tables were needed?

Reading the problem carefully shows that each table seats five couples or 10 people. At first glance, this problem might be solved using division; however, this would result in a decimal fraction, which is not useful in dealing with people seated at tables:

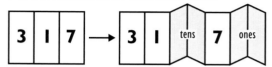

In contrast, a full understanding of numbers allows 317 to be renamed as 31 tens and 7 ones:

This provides for all the people at the party and analysis of the number 317 shows that there needs to be at least 32 tables for everyone to have a seat and allow party goers to move around and sit with others during the evening. Understanding how to *rename* a number has provided a direct solution without any need for computation. It highlights how coming to terms with a problem and integrating this with number sense provides a means of solving the problem more directly and allows an appreciation of what the solution might mean.

Spatial sense is equally important as information is frequently presented in visual formats that need to be interpreted and processed, while the use of diagrams is often essential in developing conceptual understanding across all aspects of mathematics. Using diagrams, placing information in tables or depicting a systematic way of dealing with the various possibilities in a problem assist in visualising what is happening. It can be a very powerful tool in coming to terms with the information in a problem and it provides insight into ways to proceed to a solution.

Spatial sense involves:
- a capacity to visualise shapes and their properties
- determining relationships among shapes and their properties
- linking two-dimensional and three-dimensional representations
- presenting and interpreting information in tables and lists
- an inclination to use diagrams and models to visualise problem situations and applications in flexible ways.

The following problem shows how these understandings can be used.

> *A small sheet of paper has been folded in half and then cut along the fold to make two rectangles.*
>
> *The perimeter of each rectangle is 18 cm.*
>
> *What was the perimeter of the original square sheet of paper?*

Reading the problem carefully and analysing the diagram shows that the length of the longer side of the rectangle is the same as one side of the square while the other side of the rectangle is half this length. Another way to obtain this insight is to make a square, fold it in half along the cutting line and then fold it again. This shows that the large square is made up of four smaller squares:

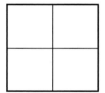

Since each rectangle contains two small squares, the perimeter of the rectangle, 18 cm, is the same as 6 sides of the smaller square, so the side of the small square is 3 cm. The perimeter of the large square is made of 8 of these small sides, so is 24 cm.

Similar thinking is used with arrangements of two-dimensional and three-dimensional shapes and in visualising how they can fit together or be taken apart.

> *Many dice are made in the shape of a cube with arrangements of dots on each square face so that the sum of the dots on opposite faces is always 7. An arrangement of squares that can be folded to make a cube is called a net of a cube.*

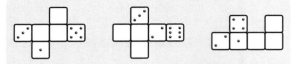

> *Which of these arrangements of squares forms a net for the dice?*

> *Greengrocers often stack fruit as a pyramid.*
>
> *How many oranges are in this stack?*

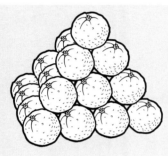

Measurement sense is dependent on both number sense and spatial sense as attributes that are one-, two- or three-dimensional are quantified to provide both exact and approximate measures and allow comparison. Many measurements use aspects of space (length, area, volume), while others use numbers on a scale (time, mass, temperature). Money can be viewed as a measure of value and uses numbers more directly, while practical activities such as map reading and determining angles require a sense of direction as well as gauging measurement. The coordination of the thinking for number and space, along with an understanding of how the metric system builds on place value, zero and renaming, is critical in both building measurement understanding and using it to come to terms with and solve many practical problems and applications.

Measurement sense includes:

- understanding how numeration and computation underpin measurement
- extending relationships from number understandings to the metric system
- appreciating the relative size of measurements
- a capacity to use calculators, mental or written processes for exact and approximate calculations
- an inclination to use understanding and facility with measurements in flexible ways.

The following problem shows how these understandings can be used.

A city square has an area of 160 m². Four small triangular garden beds are constructed from each corner to the midpoints of the sides of the square. What is the area of each garden bed?

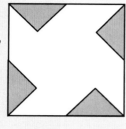

Reading the problem carefully shows that there are 4 garden beds and each of them takes up the same proportions of the whole square. A quick look at the area of the square shows that there will not be an exact number of metres along one side. Some further thinking will be needed to determine the area of each garden bed.

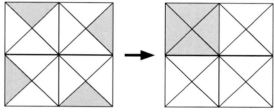

If the midpoints of each side are drawn across the square, four smaller squares are formed and each garden bed takes up $\frac{1}{4}$ of a small square. Four of the garden beds will have the same area of one small square. Since area of the small square is $\frac{1}{4}$ the area of the large square, the area of one small square is 40 m² and the area of each triangular garden bed is 10 m².

An understanding of the problem situation given by a diagram has been integrated with spatial thinking and a capacity to calculate mentally with simple fractions to provide an appropriate solution. Both spatial sense and number sense have been used to understand the problem and suggest a means to a solution.

Data sense is an outgrowth of measurement sense and refers to an understanding of the way number sense, spatial sense and a sense of measurement work together to deal with situations where patterns need to be discerned among data or when likely outcomes need to be analysed. This can occur among frequencies in data or possibilities in chance.

Data sense involves:

- understanding how numeration and computation underpin the analysis of data
- appreciating the relative likelihood of outcomes
- a capacity to use calculators or mental and written processes for exact and approximate calculations
- presenting and interpreting data in tables and graphs
- an inclination to use understanding and facility with number combinations and arrangements in flexible ways.

The following problem shows how these understandings can be used.

A bag has five blue marbles, three red marbles and four yellow marbles. How many red marbles need to be added to the bag so that the probability of drawing a red marble is $\frac{3}{4}$?

An understanding of probability and careful analysis of the situation are needed to come to terms with what the problem is asking. If the probability of drawing a red marble is $\frac{3}{4}$, then the probability of drawing a blue or yellow marble must be $\frac{1}{4}$. There are nine blue or yellow marbles, so there would need to be 36 marbles altogether to give the probability of $\frac{1}{4}$ and all the other marbles must be red. 27 of the marbles would have to be red, so another 24 red marbles need to be added to the bag. A systematic consideration of the possible outcomes has allowed a solution to be developed.

Patterning is another critical aspect of sense making in mathematics. Often a problem calls on discerning a pattern in the placement of materials, the numbers involved in the situation or the possible arrangements of data or outcomes so as to determine a likely solution. Being able to see patterns is also very helpful in getting a solution more immediately or understanding whether or not a solution is complete.

A farmer had emus and alpacas in one paddock. When she counted, there were 38 heads and 100 legs. How many emus and how many alpacas are in the paddock?

There are 38 emus and alpacas. Emus have 2 legs. Alpacas have 4 legs.

Number of alpacas	Number of emus	Number of legs
4	34	84 – too few
8	30	92 – too few
10	28	96 – too few
12	26	100

There are 12 alpacas and 26 emus.

As more experience in solving problems is gained, an ability to see patterns in what is occurring will also allow solutions to be obtained more directly and help in seeing the relationship between a new problem and one that has been solved previously. It is this ability to relate problem types, even when the context appears to be quite different, that often distinguishes a good problem-solver from one who is more hesitant.

Building a problem-solving process

While the teaching of problem-solving has often centred on the use of particular strategies that could apply to various classes of problems, many pupils are unable to access and use these strategies to solve problems outside of the teaching situations in which they were introduced. Rather than acquire a process for solving problems, they may attempt to memorise a set of procedures and view mathematics as a set of learned rules where success follows the use of the right procedure to the numbers given in the problem. Any use of strategies may be based on familiarity, personal preference or recent exposure rather than through a consideration of the problem to be solved. A pupil may even feel it is sufficient to have only one strategy and that the strategy should work all of the time; and if it doesn't, then the problem 'can't be done'.

In contrast, observation of successful problem-solvers shows that their success depends more on an analysis of the problem itself—what is being asked, what information might be used, what answer might be likely and so on—so that a particular approach is used only after the intent of the problem is determined. Establishing the meaning of the problem before any plan is drawn up or work on a solution begins is critical. Pupils need to see that discussion about the problem's meaning, and the ways of obtaining a solution, must take precedence over a focus on 'the answer'. Using collaborative groups when problem-solving, rather than tasks assigned individually, is an approach that helps to develop this disposition.

Looking at a problem and working through what is needed to solve it will shed light on the problem-solving process.

Great Grandma Jean left £93 000 in her will. She asked that it be shared out so that each of her three great grandchildren received the same amount, their  *father (her grandson) twice as much as the three grandchildren together, and her daughter (the children's grandmother) £3000 more than the father and great grandchildren together. How much does each get?*

Reading the problem carefully shows that Great Grandma left her money to her daughter, grandson and three great grandchildren. She arranged her will so that her daughter was given £3000 before the remaining £90 000 was distributed so that the amounts given to the grandson is twice that given to her great grandchildren, while the amount she gets is equal to the sum given to all the others. All of the required information to solve the problem is available and no further information is needed. The question at the end asks how much money each gets, but really the problem is how the money was distributed among all the beneficiaries of her will.

The discussion of this problem serves to identify the key elements within the problem-solving process. To commence it was necessary to *analyse* the problem to unfold its meanings and discover what needs to be considered. What the problem is asking is rarely found in the problem statement. In this phase, it is necessary to look below the surface level of the problem and come to terms with the problem's structure. Reading the problem aloud, recalling of previous difficult problems and other similar problems, selecting the important information from the problem that may be useful and discussion of the problem's meaning are all essential.

The next step is to *explore* possible ways to solve the problem. If the analysis stage has been completed, then ways in which it might be solved will emerge. It is here that strategies and how they might be useful to solving a problem can arise. However, most problems can be solved in a variety of ways, using different approaches, and a pupil needs to be encouraged to select a means that make sense and appears achievable to him or her.

Possible ways that come to mind during the analysis are:

Materials – counters could be used to represent each £1000. Then work backwards through the problem from when £3000 was kept aside for the daughter.

Try and adjust – Trial an amount that the great grandchildren might have received. Calculate the amounts and then adjust, if necessary, until the full £90 000 is allocated.

Backtrack using the numbers – her grandson received twice as much as the 3 great grandchildren, while her daughter received as much as her grandson and great grandchildren combined. The amount distributed to all the beneficiaries must be twice the amount given to her daughter.

Use a diagram to represent the information in the problem.

Think of a similar problem – for example, is it like a problem you have previously encountered and solved? If so, use similar reasoning to solve this problem.

Now one of the possible means to a solution can be selected to *try*. Backtracking shows that £90 000 was double what was given to the daughter, so she must have received £45 000 in addition to the £3000 already allocated. The other £45 000 was given to the grandson and three great grandchildren so that the amount given to the grandson was double that given to the great grandchildren. The grandson must have received £30 000 and the total given to the three great grandchildren was half of this amount or £15 000. Each great grandchild must have been given £5000.

Materials could also have been used to work backwards. Ninety counters represent the £90 000 to be distributed, so 45 would be allocated to the daughter. The other 45 counters have to be split so that the grandson gets twice as much as the great grandchildren, 30 must be given to the grandson and 15 to the great grandchildren—they would receive 5 counters each.

Another way to solve this problem is with a diagram. If we use a rectangle to represent the £90 000 left after the daughter got the additional £3000, we can show by shading how much was given to the others:

She received as much as the others combined, so must have received half:

£45 000	

The father got twice as much as the great grandchildren, and so received two-thirds of the remainder:

	£45 000	

The great grandchildren each received an equal share of the remaining £15 000:

	£45 000	

Each of the 9 equal parts represents £45 000, so each great grandchild receives £5000.

Having tried an idea, the answer(s) and solution need to be analysed in light of the problem in case another solution or answer is needed. It is essential to compare an answer back to the original analysis of the problem to determine whether the solution obtained is reasonable and answers the problem. It will also raise the question as to whether other answers exist, and if there may be other solution strategies. In this way, the process is cyclic and should the answer be unreasonable, then the process would need to begin again.

If each great grandchild received £5000, then the grandson received twice as much as the 3 great grandchildren (£30 000). The daughter received the same as the grandson and three great grandchildren (or £45 000 and another £3000). The total distributed is £93 000. Looking back at the problem, we see that this is correct and that the diagram has provided a direct means to the solution that has minimised and simplified the calculations.

Thinking about how the various ways this problem was solved highlights the key elements within the problem-solving process. When starting the process, it is necessary to *analyse* the problem to unfold its layers, discover its structure and what the problem was really asking. Next, all possible ways to solve the problem were *explored* before one, or a combination of ways, was/were selected to *try*. Finally, once something was tried, it was important to check the solution in relation to the problem to see if the solution was reasonable. This process highlights the cyclic nature of problem-solving and brings to the fore the importance of understanding the problem (and its structure) before proceeding. This process can be summarised as:

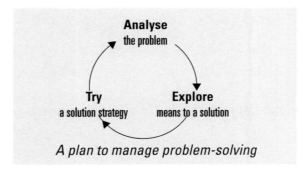

A plan to manage problem-solving

This model for problem-solving provides pupils with a means of talking about the steps they engage with whenever they have a problem to solve: Discussing how they initially analysed the problem, explored various ways that might provide a solution, and then tried one or more possible solution paths to obtain a solution—that they analysed for completeness and sense making—reinforces the very methods that will give them success on future problems. This process brings to the fore the importance of understanding the problem and its structure before proceeding.

Further, returning to an analysis of any answers and solution strategies highlights the importance of reflecting on what has been done. Taking time to reflect on any plans drawn up, processes followed and strategies used brings out the significance of coming to terms with the nature of the problem, as well as the value and applicability of particular approaches that might be used with other problems. Thinking of how a related problem was solved is often the key to solving another problem at a later stage. It allows the thinking to be 'carried over' to the new situation in a way that simply trying to think of the strategy used often fails to reveal. Analysing problems in this way also highlights that a problem is not solved until any answer obtained can be justified. Learning to reflect on the *whole* process leads to the development of a deeper understanding of problem-solving, and time must be allowed for reflection and discussion to fully build mathematical thinking.

Managing a problem-solving programme

Teaching problem-solving differs from many other aspects of mathematics in that collaborative work can be more productive than individual work. Pupils who may be tempted to quickly give up when working on their own can be led to see ways of proceeding when discussing a problem in a group. Therefore building greater confidence in their capacity to solve problems and learning the value of persisting with a problem in order to tease out what is required. What is discussed with their peers is more likely to be recalled when other problems are met while the observations made in the group increase the range of approaches that a pupil can access. Thus, time has to be allowed for discussion and exploration rather than ensuring that pupils spend 'time on task' as for routine activities.

Correct answers that fully solve a problem are always important, but developing a capacity to use an effective problem-solving process needs to be the highest priority. A pupil who has an answer should be encouraged to discuss his or her solution with others who believe they have a solution, rather than tell his or her answer to another pupil or simply move on to another problem. In particular, explaining to others why he or she believes an answer is reasonable, as well as why it provides a solution, gets other pupils to focus on the entire problem-solving process rather than just quickly getting an answer.

Expressing an answer in a sentence that relates to the question stated in the problem also encourages reflection on what was done and ensures that the focus is on solving the problem rather than providing an answer. These aspects of the teaching of problem-solving should then be taken further, as particular groups discuss their solutions with the whole class and all pupils are able to participate in the discussion of the problem. In this way, problem-solving as a way of thinking comes to the fore, rather than focusing on the answers to a series of problems that some pupils see as the main aim of their mathematical activities.

Questions need to encourage pupils to explore possible means to a solution and try one or more of them, rather than point to a particular procedure. It can also assist pupils to see how to progress their thinking, rather than get in a loop where the same steps are repeated over and over. However, while having too many questions that focus on the way to a solution may end up removing the problem-solving aspect from the question, having too few may cause pupils to become frustrated with the task and think that it is beyond them. Pupils need to experience the challenge of problem-solving and gain pleasure from working through the process that leads to a full solution. Taking time to listen to pupils as they try out their ideas, without comment or without directing them to a particular strategy, is also important. Listening provides a sense of how pupils' problem solving is developing, as assessing this aspect of mathematics can be difficult. After all, solving one problem will not necessarily lead to success on the next problem, nor will a difficulty with a particular problem mean that the problems that follow will also be as challenging.

A teacher may also need to extend or adapt a given problem to ensure the problem-solving process is understood and can be used in other situations, instead of moving on to another different problem in the way that one example or topic shifts to another in other parts of mathematics learning. This can help pupils to understand the significance of asking questions of a problem, as well as seeing how a way of thinking can be adapted to other related problems. Having pupils engage in this process of problem posing is another way of both assessing and bringing them to terms with the overall process of solving problems.

Building a problem-solving process

The cyclical model, *Analyse–Explore–Try*, provides a very helpful means of organising and discussing possible solutions. However, care must be taken that it is not seen simply as a procedure to be memorised and then applied in a routine manner to every new problem. Rather, it needs to be carefully developed over a range of different problems, highlighting the components that are developed with each new problem.

Analyse

- As pupils read a problem, the need to first read for the *meaning* of the problem can be stressed. This may require reading more than once and can be helped by asking pupils to state in their own words what the problem is asking them to do.

- Further reading will be needed to sort out which information is needed and whether some is not needed or if other information needs to be gathered from the problem's context (e.g. data presented within the illustration or table accompanying the problem), or whether the pupils' mathematical understandings need to be used to find other relationships among the information. As the form of the problems becomes more complex, this thinking will be extended to incorporate further ways of dealing with the information; for example, measurement units, fractions and larger numbers might need to be renamed to the same mathematical form.

- Thinking about any processes that might be needed and the order in which they are used, as well as the type of answer that could occur, should also be developed in the context of new levels of problem structure.

- Developing a capacity to see 'through' the problem's expression—or context to see similarities between new problems and others that might already have been met—is a critical way of building expertise in coming to terms with and solving problems.

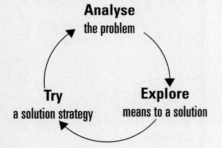

Expanding the problem-solving process

A fuller model to manage problem-solving can gradually emerge:

- Read carefully.
- What is the problem asking?
- What is the meaning of the information? Is it all needed? Is there too little? Too much?
- Which operations will be needed and in what order?
- What sort of answer is likely?
- Have I seen a problem like this before?

- Put the solution back into the problem.
- Does the answer make sense?
- Does it solve the problem?
- Is it the only answer?
- Could there be another way?

Analyse
the problem

Try
a solution strategy

Explore
means to a solution

- Use materials or a model.
- Use a calculator.
- Use pencil and paper.
- Look for a pattern.

- Use a diagram or materials.
- Work backwards or backtrack.
- Put the information into a table.
- Try and adjust.

Explore

- When a problem is being explored, some problems will require the use of materials to think through the whole of the problem's context. Others will demand the use of diagrams to show what is needed. Another will show how systematic analysis of the situation using a sequence of diagrams, on a list or table, is helpful. As these ways of thinking about the problem are understood, they can be included in the cycle of steps.

Try

- Many pupils often try to guess a result. This can even be encouraged by talking about 'guess and check' as a means to solve problems. Changing to 'try and adjust' is more helpful in building a way of thinking and can lead to a very powerful way of finding solutions.

- When materials, a diagram or table have been used, another means to a solution is to look for a pattern in the results. When these have revealed what is needed to try for a solution, it may also be reasonable to use pencil and paper or a calculator.

Analyse

- The point in the cycle where an answer is assessed for reasonableness (e.g. whether it provides a solution, is only one of several solutions or whether there may be another way to solve the problem) also needs to be brought to the fore as different problems are met.

The role of calculators

When calculators are used, pupils devote less time to basic calculations, providing time that might be needed to either explore a solution or find an answer to a problem. In this way, attention is shifted from computation, which the calculator can do, to thinking about the problem and its solution—work that the calculator cannot do. It also allows more problems (and more realistic problems) to be addressed in problem-solving sessions. In these situations, a calculator serves as a tool rather than a crutch, requiring pupils to think through the problem's solution in order to know how to use the calculator appropriately. It also underpins the need to make sense of the steps along the way and any answers that result, as keying incorrect numbers, operations or order of operations quickly leads to results that are not appropriate.

Choosing, adapting and extending problems

When problems are selected, they need to be examined to see if pupils already have an understanding of the underlying mathematics required and that the problem's expression can be meaningfully read by the group of pupils who will be attempting the solution—though not necessarily by *all* pupils in the group. The problem itself should be neither too easy (so that it is just an exercise, repeating something readily done before), nor too difficult (thus beyond the capabilities of most or all in the group), and engages the interests of the pupils. A problem should also be able to be solved in more than one way.

As a problem and its solution is reviewed, posing similar questions—where the numbers, shapes or measurements are changed—focuses attention back on what was entailed in analysing the problem and in exploring the means to a solution. Extending these processes to more complex situations enables the particular approach used to extend to other situations and shows how to analyse patterns to obtain more general methods or results. It also highlights the importance of a systematic approach when conceiving and discussing a solution and can lead to pupils asking themselves further questions about the situation, thus posing problems of their own as the significance of the problem's structure is uncovered.

Problem structure and expression

When analysing a problem it is also possible to discern critical aspects of the problem's form and relate this to an appropriate level of mathematics and problem expression when choosing or extending problems. A problem of first-level complexity uses simple mathematics and simple language. A 'second-level' may have simple language and more difficult mathematics or more difficult language and simple mathematics; while a third-level has yet more difficult language and mathematics. Within a problem, the processes that need to be used may be more or less obvious, the information that is required for a solution may be too much or too little, and strategic thinking may be needed in order to come to terms with what the problem is asking.

Level	processes obvious	processes less obvious	too much information	too little information	strategic thinking
increasing difficulty with problem's expression and mathematics required	simple expression, simple mathematics				
	more complex expression, simple mathematics				
	simple expression, more complex mathematics				
	complex expression, complex mathematics				

The varying levels of problem structure and expression

(i) The processes to be used are relatively obvious as: these problems are comparatively straightforward and contain all the information necessary to find a solution.

(ii) The processes required are not immediately obvious as these problems contain all the information necessary to find a solution but demand further analysis to sort out what is wanted and pupils may need to reverse what initially seemed to be required.

(iii) The problem contains more information than is needed for a solution as these problems contain not only all the information needed to find a solution, but also additional information in the form of times, numbers, shapes or measurements.

(iv) Further information needs to be gathered and applied to the problem in order to obtain a solution. These problems do not contain first-hand all the necessary information required to find a solution but do contain a means to obtain the required information. The problem's setting, the pupil's mathematical understanding or the problem's wording need to be searched for the additional material.

(v) Strategic thinking is required to analyse the question in order to determine a solution strategy. Deeper analysis, often aided by the use of diagrams or tables, is needed to come to terms with what the problem is asking so as to determine a means to a solution.

This analysis of the nature of problems can also serve as a means of evaluating the provision of problems within a mathematics programme. In particular, it can lead to the development of a full range of problems, ensuring they are included across all problem forms, with the mathematics and expression suited to the level of the pupils.

Assessing problem-solving

Assessment of problem-solving requires careful and close observation of pupils working in a problem-solving setting. These observations can reveal the range of problem forms and the level of complexity in the expression and underlying mathematics that a pupil is able to confidently deal with. Further analysis of these observations can show to what extent the pupil is able to analyse the question, explore ways to a solution, select one or more methods to try and then analyse any results obtained. It is the combination of two fundamental aspects—the types of problem that can be solved and the manner in which solutions are carried out—that will give a measure of a pupil's developing problem solving abilities, rather than a one-off test in which some problems are solved and others are not.

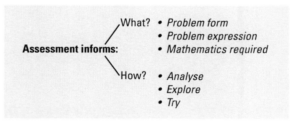

Observations based on this analysis have led to a categorisation of many of the possible difficulties that pupils experience with problem-solving as a whole, rather than the misconceptions they may have with particular problems.

These often involve inappropriate attempts at a solution based on little understanding of the problem.

A major cause of possible difficulties is the *lack of a well-developed plan* of attack, leading pupils to focus on the *surface level* of problems. In such cases, pupils:

- locate and manipulate numbers with little or no thought as to their relevance to the problem

Problem	Likely causes
Pupil is unable to make any attempt at a solution.	• lack of interest • feels overwhelmed • cannot think of how to start to answer question • needs to reconsider complexity of steps and information
Pupil has no means of linking the situation to the implicit mathematical meaning.	• needs to create diagram or use materials • needs to consider separate parts of question, then bring parts together
Pupil uses an inappropriate operation.	• misled by word cues or numbers • has underdeveloped concepts • uses rote procedures rather than real understanding
Pupil is unable to translate a problem into a more familiar process.	• cannot see interactions between operations • lack of understanding means he/she unable to reverse situations • data may need to be used in an order not evident in the problem statement or in an order contrary to that in which it is presented

- try a succession of different operations if the first ones attempted do not yield a (likely) result
- focus on keywords for an indication of what might be done without considering their significance within the problem as a whole
- read problems quickly and cursorily to locate the numbers to be used
- use the first available word cue to suggest the operation that might be needed.

Other possible difficulties result from a focus on being quick, which leads to:

- no attempt to assess the reasonableness of an answer
- little perseverance if an answer is not obtained using the first approach tried
- not being able to access strategies to which they have been introduced.

When the approaches to problem processing developed in this series are followed and the specific suggestions for solving particular problems or types of problems are discussed with pupils, these difficulties can be minimised, if not entirely avoided. Analysing the problem before starting leads to an understanding of the problem's meanings. The cycle of steps within the model means that nothing is tried before the intent of the problem is clear and the means to a solution have been considered. Focussing on a problem's meanings, and discussing what needs to be done, builds

perseverance. Making sense of the steps that need to be followed and any answers that result are central to the problem-solving process that is developed. These difficulties are unlikely among those who have built up an understanding of this way of thinking.

A final comment

If an approach to problem-solving can be built up using the ideas developed here and the problems in the investigations on the pages that follow, pupils will develop a way of thinking about and with mathematics that will allow them to readily solve problems and generalise from what they already know to understand new mathematical ideas. They will engage with these emerging mathematical conceptions from their very beginnings, be prepared to debate and discuss their own ideas, and develop attitudes that will allow them to tackle new problems and topics. Mathematics can then be a subject that is readily engaged with, and become one in which the pupil feels in control, instead of one in which many rules devoid of meaning have to be memorised and (hopefully) applied at the right time and place. This enthusiasm for learning and the ability to think mathematically will then lead to a search for meaning in new situations and processes that will allow mathematical ideas to be used across a range of applications in school and everyday life.

A NOTE ON CALCULATOR USE

Many of the problems in this series demand the use of a number of consecutive calculations, often adding, subtracting, multiplying or dividing the same amount in order to complete entries in a table or see a pattern. This demands (or will build) a certain amount of sophisticated use of the memory and constant functions of a simple calculator.

1. To add a number such as 9 repeatedly, it is sufficient on most calculators to enter an initial number (e.g. 30) then press + 9 = = = = to add 9 over and over.

   - *30, 39, 48, 57, 66, ...*

   - *To add 9 to a range of numbers, enter the first number (e.g. 30) then press + 9 = 30 + 9 = 39, 7 = gives 16, 3 = gives 12, 21 = gives 30, ...*

   - *These are the answers when 9 is added to each number.*

2. To subtract a number such as 5 repeatedly, it is sufficient on most calculators to enter an initial number (e.g. 92) then press – 5 = = = = to subtract 5 over and over.

   - *92, 87, 82, 77, 72, ...*

   - *To subtract 5 from a range of numbers, enter the first number (e.g. 92) then press – 5 = 95 – 5 = 90, 68 = gives 63, 43 = gives 38, 72 = gives 67, ...*

   - *These are the answers when 5 is subtracted from each number.*

3. To multiply a number such as 10 repeatedly, most calculators now reverse the order in which the numbers are entered. Enter 10 x, then press an initial number (e.g. 15) = = = = to multiply by 10 over and over.

   - *10, 150, 1500, 15 000, 150 000, ...*

   - *This also allows squaring of numbers: 4 x = gives 16.*

   - *Continuing to press = gives more powers:*

   - *4 x = = gives 64, 4 x = = = gives 256; 4 x = = = = gives 1024 and so on.*

   - *To multiply a range of numbers by 10, enter 10 x then the first number (e.g. 90) and =*

   - *10 x 90 = 900, 45 = gives 450, 21 = gives 210, 162 = gives 1620, ...*

   - *These are the answers when each number is multiplied by 10.*

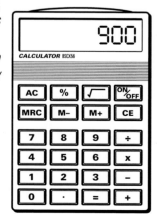

4. To divide by a number such as 4 repeatedly, enter a number (e.g. 128).

   - *Then press ÷ 4 = = = = to divide each result by 4.*

   - *32, 8 , 2, 0.5, ...*

   - *These are the answers when the given number is divided by 4.*

5. Using the memory keys M+, M– and MR will also simplify calculations. A result can be calculated and added to memory (M+). Then a second result can be calculated and added to (M+) or subtracted from (M–) the result in the memory. Pressing MR will display the result. Often this will need to be performed for several examples as they are entered onto a table or patterns are explored directly. Clearing the memory after each completed calculation is essential!

   A number of calculations may also need to be made before addition, subtraction, multiplication or division with a given number. That number can be placed in memory and used each time without needing to be re-keyed.

6. The % key can be used to find percentage increases and decreases directly.

   - *To increase or decrease a number by a certain per cent (e.g. 20%), simply key the number and press + 20% or – 20% to get the answer:*

   - *80 + 20% gives 96 (not 100) – 20% of 80 is 16, 80 + 16 is 96.*

   - *90 – 20% gives 72 (not 70) – 20% of 90 is 18, 90 – 18 is 72.*

7. While the square root key can be used directly, finding other roots is best done by a 'try and adjust' approach using the multiplication constant described above (in point 3).

Problem-solving in mathematics

Pupil worksheets and teachers notes

Problem-solving

To use spatial visualisation and logical reasoning to solve problems

Curriculum links

England (Year 6 progression to Year 7)
- Using and applying: Solve problems by breaking down complex calculations into simpler steps.
- Using and applying: Choose and use operations and calculation strategies appropriate to the numbers and context.
- Using and applying: Use step-by-step deductions to solve problems involving shapes.
- Measuring: Calculate the volume and surface area of cubes and cuboids.

Northern Ireland (Key Stage 2)
- Processes in maths: Plan and organise their work, learning to work systematically.
- Processes in maths: Develop a range of strategies for problem solving, looking for ways to overcome difficulties.
- Processes in maths: Recognise general patterns and relationships and make predictions about them.
- Measures: Develop skills in estimation of volume and area.
- Measures: Use the four operations to solve measures problems.
- Measures: Calculate the areas and volumes of shapes.

Scotland (Third)
- +/−/×/÷: Use a variety of methods to solve number problems, clearly communicating my processes and solutions.
- +/−/×/÷: Recall number facts quickly and use them accurately when making calculations.
- Measurement: Solve practical problems by applying knowledge of measure and using a formula to calculate area or volume.
- Measurement: Find the area of 2-D shapes and the volume of 3-D objects, applying knowledge to solve practical problems.

Wales (Key Stage 3)
- Skills: Select and use the mathematics, units of measure, sequences of operation and methods of computation to solve problems.
- Skills: Break complex problems into a series of tasks.
- Skills: Use a range of mental, written and calculator computational strategies.
- Skills: Interpret mathematical information presented in a variety of forms.
- Measures and money: Find areas and volumes of shapes.

Materials

cubes, calculator

Focus

These pages explore arrangements of cubes and longer shapes in order to determine surface areas and volumes and to investigate the patterns they exhibit. Spatial as well as logical thinking and organisation are involved as pupils visualise a given shape in terms of its component parts.

Discussion

Page 3

Pupils need to visualise how the items are stacked, determine which surfaces are on the outside and calculate the sum of all the areas. When the builder decided to paint all of the outside faces, there will be an additional ten 2 m x 20 cm rectangles to be painted. Care will be needed to ensure all units used are the same (metres expressed as decimal fractions or centimetres). When the 3 x 3 cube is considered, there will be one 1 cm³ in the middle—when it is removed to create the hole all the way through the cube, the surface area painted will be 6 cm² less. The 4 x 4 cube will have a 2 x 2 cube in the middle—the

surface area will be 24 cm² less when this is removed to make the hole. There are different possibilities for the 5 x 5 cube according to whether the hole is 1 cm x 1 cm or 3 cm x 3 cm when cubes are removed to make the same hole from all 6 sides. Pupils may need to use cubes to see what is happening.

Page 4

This set of investigations requires visualising the arrangement of the cubes in the inside of the prism and then seeing how there is another layer on each side to give the whole prism.

An understanding of prime factors is needed to determine the inside shape. Stacking cubes to form the inside shapes will then assist pupils to understand what is required in these problems. In the first problem, 105 has prime factors 3 x 5 x 7 which gives the dimensions of the inside, unpainted shape. Another layer on each side shows that the whole prism is 5 x 7 x 9 and the surface area is

(2 x 35) + (2 x 45) + (2 x 63) or 286 cm².

363 has prime factors 3 x 11 x 11 and can be solved in a similar manner.

60 has prime factors 2 x 2 x 3 x 5. These need to be considered 3 at a time to give four possible answers:

	4 x 3 x 5
	2 x 6 x 5
	2 x 2 x 15
or	2 x 3 x 10

Page 5

This set of investigations encourages pupils to see 3-dimensional shapes in terms of the component cubes and work out the surface area by determining the number of exposed faces and the volume by working out the total number of cubes. The cubes vary in size so other factors also come into the calculations. Pupils need to work directly from a diagram that shows how the cubes are arranged and from plans that use a grid to indicate the number of cubes in each position. The final investigation requires pupils to make a shape of their own, construct a plan and then give the plan to another pupil who has to determine the surface area and volume of the shape.

Possible difficulties

- Unable to visualise the 3-dimensional shapes from the information given
- Does not realise the internal prisms are given by considering the prime factors of the number of cubes
- Does not take into account the dimension of the different cubes when working out volumes
- Does not consider all of the surfaces when working out surface areas

Extension

- Investigate other arrangements of railway sleepers to make steps.
- Reverse the problem with the prisms: if 429 715 or 1001 cubes were used to make a rectangular prism which was then painted yellow on the outside, how many cubes would not be painted? What would be the volume and surface area of the unpainted prism?
- Have pupils make up their own problems like the last problem on page 3; e.g. 36 unpainted cubes of side 3 cm, 48 unpainted cubes of side 2 cm or 64 unpainted cubes of side 4 cm.

SURFACE AREA

1. Some 2 m long railway sleepers with 10 cm x 20 cm rectangular ends are going to be stacked to form a set of garden stairs with 5 steps. If all the exposed sides except those on the bottom and on the higher end set into the garden are painted with wood preserver, what area will be painted?

_____

_____

2. When the builder put the steps together, he decided to paint all the outside surfaces before he assembled the steps in order to prolong the life of the stairs. What area did he actually paint?

_____

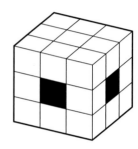

3. Imagine 1 cm³ cubes stacked to make a 3 x 3 x 3 cube. Remove one cube from the centre of each face. If all of the exposed faces are painted red, what is the surface area of the shape that has been painted?

_____

4. Would the surface area to be painted change if there was a hole through the centre of the cube?

_____

5. (a) Now imagine a 4 x 4 x 4 cube. Remove a square of cubes from the centre of each face. What would be the surface area of this shape?

_____

   (b) How would the surface area change if there was a hole in the centre of this cube?

_____

6. If you had a 5 x 5 x 5 cube and removed a square of cubes from the centre of each face, what surface area could there be? (There are 2 possibilities.)

_____

_____

7. How would the surface area change if there was a hole in the centre of the cube? (Consider all the possibilities.)

_____

_____

VOLUME AND SURFACE AREA

1. A number of 1 cm³ cubes are put together to make a rectangular prism with each edge greater than 1 cm. The six faces of the prism are painted green. When the small cubes are taken apart, 105 have no paint on them.

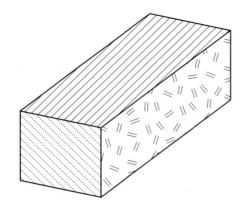

(a) Where would these cubes occur?

_____

_____

(b) What shape would they form?

_____

Use this information to find:

(c) the volume of the whole prism   _____

(d) the surface area of the whole prism.   _____

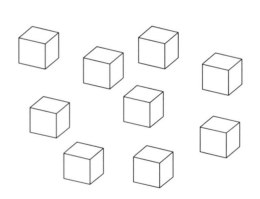

2. A large number of 1 cm³ cubes are put together to make another rectangular prism with edges greater than 1 cm. After the six faces of the prism are painted green and then taken apart, 363 of the small cubes have not been painted.

What is the volume and surface area of the whole prism?

_____

_____

3. Some 2 cm³ cubes are put together to make a rectangular prism. The six faces of the prism are painted blue. When the small cubes are taken apart, 60 have no paint on them.

(a) In which ways could 60 cubes form the internal prism?

_____

_____

(b) What would be the volume and surface area of the whole prism for each possibility?

_____

_____

_____

SURFACE AREA AND VOLUME

1. Some 2 cm³ cubes have been arranged to make this shape.

   (a) What is the surface area of the shape?

   _____

   (b) What is the volume of the shape?

   _____

   (c) If you add one more block to the upper
   surface of every block, what will be the
   new surface area and volume?

   _____

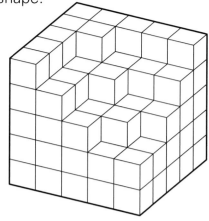

6	6	4	2
7	6	4	
6	5	3	
5	4		

2. Here is a plan of a shape made from a
   number of 3 cm³ cubes. The squares show
   where the cubes are and the numbers show
   how many cubes at each place.

   (a) Get the number of cubes you will need and make the shape. Use this model to
   work out the surface area and volume of the shape.

   _____

   (b) Work out the surface area and volume of the shapes shown by these plans. The
   size of the cubes is written underneath each plan.

   (i)

5	4	3	2	1
4	6	6	4	2
3	2	1	1	1

   2 cm³ cubes

   (ii)

6	3		
5	3		
5	3		
4	3	2	1
4	3	2	1

   3 cm³ cubes

   (iii)

5	3	2	4
3	5	4	2
2	4	5	3
4	2	3	5

   4 cm³ cubes

   _____   _____   _____

   (c) Can you work out the volume and surface area directly from the plan? (You may
   need to draw the views from each side and the top to find the surface area.)

   (d) Make a shape of your own. Then make a plan for it and decide on the dimensions
   of the cubes. Ask a friend to work out the surface area and volume. Does your
   friend need to make the shape?

Problem-solving

To use logical reasoning and number sense to solve problems

Curriculum links

England (Year 6 progression to Year 7)
- Using and applying: Solve problems by breaking down complex calculations into simpler steps.
- Using and applying: Choose and use operations and calculation strategies appropriate to the numbers and context.
- Using and applying: Represent information or unknown numbers in a problem; for example, in a table.

Northern Ireland (Key Stage 2)
- Processes in maths: Plan and organise their work, learning to work systematically.
- Processes in maths: Develop a range of strategies for problem solving, looking for ways to overcome difficulties.
- Processes in maths: Present information and results clearly.
- Number: Use the four operations to solve problems.

Scotland (Third)
- +/-/x/÷: Use a variety of methods to solve number problems, clearly communicating my processes and solutions.
- +/-/x/÷: Recall number facts quickly and use them accurately when making calculations.

Wales (Key Stage 3)
- Skills: Select and use the mathematics, sequences of operation and methods of computation to solve problems.
- Skills: Select, trial and evaluate a variety of approaches.
- Skills: Break complex problems into a series of tasks.
- Skills: Use a range of mental, written and calculator computational strategies.
- Skills: Interpret mathematical information presented in a variety of forms.

Materials

counters

Focus

This page explores problems based on a conceptual understanding of whole numbers and fractions and an understanding of what makes sense in the problem contexts. Backtracking from the final position will assist in understanding and solving the problems but counters could also be used to keep track of what is happening. Using a diagram or calculator are other ways to sort through the information while keeping the intent of the problem in mind.

Discussion

Page 7

These problems highlight the need to carefully analyse the problem before starting on a solution. In the first problem, more than half the avocados are sold on the Saturday if 25 less than half is sold on the Sunday. One way to solve the problem involves 'Try and adjust' using a table to keep track:

	Saturday	Sunday	total sold
Try	300	125	425 – too few
Try	400	175	575 – too many
Try	390	170	560 – too few
Try	398	174	572

A form of algebraic reasoning is another way.

The number sold on Sunday is (half the number sold on Saturday – 25).

The number sold, 572, is the number sold on Saturday + (half the number sold on Saturday – 25).

1.5 x the number sold on Saturday – 25 is 572, so 3 x the number sold on Saturday – 50 is 1144.

3 x the number sold on Saturday is 1194.

398 avocados are sold on Saturday.

In the second problem, clearly Lance is not actually going to sell half a tomato! At each step, there must be an odd number of tomatoes. When he sells these tomatoes, they will both get half of the nearest even number and the customer will get 1 extra tomato. This means that before Lance sold the last tomatoes, the third customer must have taken 56 leaving Lance 55 tomatoes to sell. The customer before that must have taken 112 leaving Lance 111 tomatoes to sell. So the first customer took 224 tomatoes leaving Lance 223 tomatoes to sell. Lance started with 447 tomatoes:

Lance	third customer	Lance	second customer	Lance	first customer	Lance
55	56					
		111	112			
				223	224	
						447

The third problem is similar to the second problem but this time the seller must add 3 to the number of pumpkins left to find half of the number he had to sell. Counters, a diagram similar to Problem 2 or a table for 'Try and adjust' show this readily.

Try	Lance	First	Lance	Second	Lance	Third	Lance/last
50	22	27	8	14	1	7	too few
60	27	33	X				
58	26	32	10	16	2	13	too few
62	28	34	11	17	X		
64	29		X				
66	30	36	12	18	3	9	3

He brought 66 pumpkins to the market.

Possible difficulties

- Unable to see how the half tomato or pumpkin or extra tomatoes or pumpkins fit into the problems
- Simply working on the basis of calculations with the numbers in the problem to obtain incorrect answers

Extension

- Change the numbers in the problems but leave the problem statements the same:
  - More avocados for sale, a different amount more or less than 1 half, 1 third, 3 quarters, ...
  - More avocados or pumpkins at the end of the sale or 3, 4 or 5 more each time.
- Have pupils make up problems like these of their own and challenge others to solve them using diagrams, tables for try and adjust or algebraic thinking.

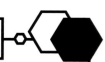

THE FARMERS MARKET

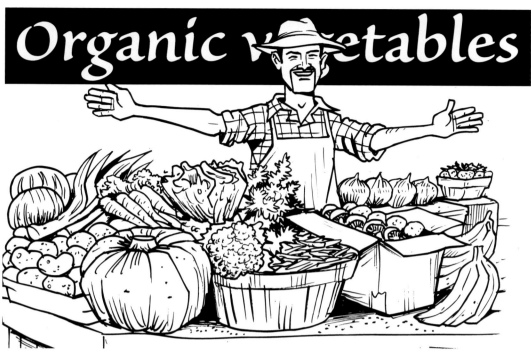

1. Lance grows and sells organic vegetables at the local farmers market. He sold 572 avocados at the two markets held last weekend. When he took stock on Sunday night, he noticed that the number of avocados he sold on Sunday was 25 less than half the number he sold at the Saturday market. How many avocados did he sell at each market?

_____

_____

2. Lance is really well known for his luscious tomatoes. On Saturday, he sold half of his tomatoes and another half a tomato to his first customer, half the remaining tomatoes and another half a tomato to his second customer, half the remainder and another half a tomato to his third customer. He then sold the remaining 55 tomatoes to the woman who ran the sandwich stall. How many tomatoes did he have to start with?

_____

_____

3. As the weather had turned cold, people wanted to make soup and there was a rush on pumpkins as soon as Lance opened his market stall. The first customer bought half the pumpkins he had brought to the market and three more pumpkins. His next customer bought half of those pumpkins and another three pumpkins. The third customer bought half of what he had left and another three pumpkins. The fourth customer quickly bought the last three pumpkins. How many pumpkins did he bring to the market to sell? (Lance only sold whole pumpkins as he found it too hard to cut them in half—he always got two unequal parts.)

_____

_____

Problem-solving
To read, interpret and analyse information

Curriculum links
England (Year 6 progression to Year 7)
- Using and applying: Solve problems by breaking down complex calculations into simpler steps.
- Using and applying: Choose and use operations and calculation strategies appropriate to the numbers and context.
- Using and applying: Represent information or unknown numbers in a problem; for example, in a table.

Northern Ireland (Key Stage 2)
- Processes in maths: Plan and organise their work, learning to work systematically.
- Processes in maths: Develop a range of strategies for problem solving, looking for ways to overcome difficulties.
- Processes in maths: Present information and results clearly.
- Number: Develop an understanding of place value.
- Number: Understand and use the terms square and cube.
- Number: Use the four operations to solve problems.
- Number: Use the four operations to solve problems involving money.

Scotland (Third)
- +/-/x/÷: Use a variety of methods to solve number problems, clearly communicating my processes and solutions.
- +/-/x/÷: Recall number facts quickly and use them accurately when making calculations.

Wales (Key Stage 3)
- Skills: Select and use the mathematics, sequences of operation and methods of computation to solve problems.
- Skills: Break complex problems into a series of tasks.
- Skills: Use a range of mental, written and calculator computational strategies.
- Skills: Interpret mathematical information presented in a variety of forms.
- Number: Use a calculator efficiently.

Materials
calculator

Focus
These pages explore concepts of place value, number sense and using data. The relationships among numbers and place value is analysed and pupils are encouraged to not only find possibilities but to also disregard numbers and combinations that are not possible. Data needs to be interpreted and analysed to find solutions. See the note on using a calculator (page xx) for ways to use the different functions.

Discussion
Page 9
This investigation requires pupils to read and interpret information and use this information to find a solution. Pupils need to think in terms of fixed costs occurring regardless of income and variable costs occurring according to production. The variable cost per item is not given as such and pupils need to use information regarding 500 items which have a variable cost of £7500 to identify that the variable cost per item is £15.

Once the table is complete the data can then be used to work out at which point the factory moves from making a loss to making a profit.

The point at which this occurs is not shown in the table and pupils need to take what they know—that she is making a loss at 100 items but making a profit at 250 and somewhere in between is where the break-even point will occur.

Page 10
These problems are easy to state and investigate using a calculator's memory function to simplify the steps and assist in developing algebraic thinking as the patterns described in words for the examples used are translated into early proofs in general. The first problem investigates a pattern based on the difference of two squares that was first used in Book E, but now the focus is on why the result would be true in general. The second problem is an investigation based on the difference of two cubes. The pattern can be discerned as the examples are worked through using the calculator, but showing why this is true in general requires quite sophisticated algebraic reasoning which should be understandable by the children but not necessarily a form of thinking they would come to by themselves.

Page 11
The puzzle scrolls contain a number of different problems, all involving strategic thinking to find possible solutions. In most cases pupils will find tables, lists and diagrams are needed to manage the data while exploring the different possibilities. In some cases the information needs to be analysed to find a pattern to find out solutions. For example, in the investigation involving '3 digit numbers adding to 6' the possible solutions from numbers in the one hundreds can then be used to determine other numbers in the 2 hundreds and so on.

The scroll exploring 3-digit numbers when dividing by 5 and 7 would mean that each number had to end in a 3 or an 8. The first 3-digit number divisible by 7 is 105. If we add 2 to this number we get 107 which can be our starting number for looking for other numbers. If we key 107 into a calculator, add 7 and press equal it will keep adding 7 each time. If we then record any numbers which end in a 3 or an 8 and we have the numbers which will result in a remainder of 3 when dividing by 5 and a remainder of 2 when dividing by 7.

For the scroll exploring the number of beads pupils can again think in terms of multiples. If they find 13 by 8 (the first 3-digit multiple of 8) which is 104, add one to this number to give the starting number. Again a calculator can be used (add 8, press the equal key and it will add 8 each time). These numbers can be recorded and pupils can then look at multiples of 7 (with 1 added) and highlight any numbers that are the same and then, from these possibilities, check to see if it is also true for 6.

Possible difficulties
- Difficulty with the concepts of fixed cost and variable costs
- Difficulty with the concept of profit and loss
- Poor understanding of place value
- Wanting to add, subtract or multiply rather than using place value or number sense
- Not using all the criteria

Extension
- Pupils could think up their own profit and loss problems using different criteria.
- Pupils could make puzzle scroll cards where they take the existing card and change the numbers or context to make a new problem.

PROFIT AND LOSS

A factory owner knows that some of her expenses are going to occur regardless of how many items she makes and sells. These are fixed costs and include things such as rent, insurance, phone and Internet. Her fixed costs total £4000 per week.

Her other expenses are variable costs which change each week depending on the number of items she makes. Variable costs include things such as materials, labour and electricity.

All factory items are made to order, so all items produced are sold. In one week she sold 500 items and her variable costs were £7500. All items sell at £50 each.

1. Complete the table below to show the income for the shop based on the number of items sold as well as the total costs for each week.

Items sold per week	50	75	100	250	500	1000	1500	3000
Income								
Total costs								

The difference between total costs and income is the factory owner's profit. If she made no sales she would still have to pay the fixed costs and would have a loss for that week.

2. Did she make a profit or a loss when she sold 100 items?

_____

3. Did she make a profit or a loss when she sold 1000 items?

_____

4. Using the information in the table, estimate the number of items she needs to sell each week to break even. Calculate the expenses and income for that number of items to check your estimate.

_____

_____

CALCULATOR PATTERNS

Use your calculator to help think about what is happening.

Squaring and multiplying

1. Choose 3 consecutive 2-digit numbers; e.g. 69, 70, 71.

   (a) Multiply the first and third numbers.

   (b) Square the middle number.

   (c) What do you notice?

   _____

   _____

   (d) Try some other 2-digit numbers.

   (e) Try some 3-digit numbers and 4-digit numbers.

   (f) Describe the pattern. Why does this happen?

   _____

   _____

Cubing, squaring and multiplying

2. Choose a 2-digit number; e.g. 47.

   (a) Make a new number by finding the difference between the cube of the tens digit and the cube of the ones digit.

   (b) Make another new number by adding the square of the tens digit, the square of the ones digit and the product of the tens and ones digits.

   (c) Divide the first new number by the second new number.

   (d) Try some other 2-digit numbers.

   (e) What do you notice?

   _____

   _____

   (f) Investigate what happens if you split a 3-digit number into 2 parts (there will be two different ways).

   _____

   _____

   (g) Describe the pattern. Can you explain why this happens?

   _____

   _____

PUZZLE SCROLLS

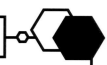

1. Five paintbrushes and 2 sets of paints cost £19.25 while 3 brushes and 2 sets of paints cost £16.75. How much does 1 set of paints cost?

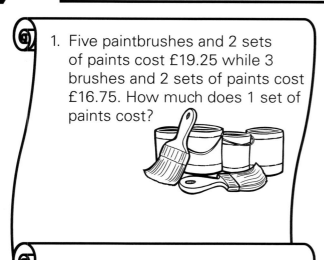

2. A box with over 100 beads can be shared among 6, 7 or 8 bags with 1 bead left over each time. What is the smallest number of beads that the box could have?

3. The number 105 has a digit sum of 6 (1 + 0 + 5). How many other 3-digit numbers have a digit sum of 6?

4. When 54 is added to a number the result is the same as when the number is multiplied by 3. What is the number?

5. What 3-digit numbers have a remainder of 3 when divided by 5 and a remainder of 2 when divided by 7? How many did you find?

6. Two cash registers had a combined total of £500. When £18 was taken from one register to the other, they each had the same amount. How much did they have before the transfer?

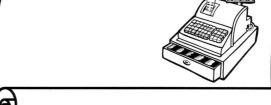

TEACHER NOTES

Problem-solving
To analyse and determine probability

Curriculum links

England (Year 6 progression to Year 7)
- Using and applying: Solve problems by breaking down complex calculations into simpler steps.
- Using and applying: Choose and use operations and calculation strategies appropriate to the numbers and context.
- Handling data: Understand and use the probability scale from 0 to 1.
- Handling data: Find and justify probabilities based on equally likely outcomes in simple contexts.

Northern Ireland (Key Stage 2)
- Processes in maths: Plan and organise their work, learning to work systematically.
- Processes in maths: Develop a range of strategies for problem solving, looking for ways to overcome difficulties.
- Processes in maths: Recognise general patterns and relationships and make predictions about them.
- Handling data: Understand, calculate and use the mean and range of a set of data.

Scotland (Third)
- +/-/x/÷: Use a variety of methods to solve number problems, clearly communicating my processes and solutions.
- Ideas of chance and uncertainty: Find the probability of a simple event happening.

Wales (Key Stage 3)
- Skills: Select and use the mathematics, sequences of operation and methods of computation to solve problems.
- Skills: Break complex problems into a series of tasks.
- Skills: Use a range of mental, written and calculator computational strategies.
- Skills: Interpret mathematical information presented in a variety of forms.
- Handling data: Calculate or estimate the mean and range of sets of data.
- Handling data: Understand and use the vocabulary of probability and the probability scale from 0 to 1.
- Handling data: Identify all the outcomes of an experiment or event.

Materials
calculator

Focus
These pages explore word problems that mostly centre around probability. Pupils need to determine what the problem is asking and in many cases carry out more than one step in order to find solutions. Analysis of the problems reveals that some problems contain additional information that is not needed. A calculator can be used to assist if necessary as these problems are about reading for information and determining what the problem is asking rather than computation or basic facts.

Discussion

Page 13
This page involves pupils reading information in a table and using that information to determine means and probabilities. The table lists a summary of weather information for Australian cities. The activity about the three cities with an average maximum temperature would involve multiplying 40 by 3 and working out which three cities would add to this total. Estimation is important at this stage so that pupils don't simply add every combination to find a solution. As the mean is 40, pupils need to take into consideration that cities with temperatures of 35, 37 and 38 would not be feasible. Another point to consider is that the mean is a whole number. As there are not 3 whole numbers in the table it needs to be two decimal numbers which add to a whole number, which narrows down the possible combinations. The investigation about the daily average rainfall requires pupils to take the total amount of rain and divide it by the number of days it rained. This will result in a daily average. Discussion could centre around what a daily average tells us, as in many cases the daily average would not be how much rain actually fell on those days.

Page 14
The investigations on this page centre around the concept of probability. The probability of an event is a number describing the chance that the event will happen. An event that is certain to happen has a probability of 1. An event that cannot possibly happen has a probability of zero. If there is a chance that an event will happen, then its probability is between zero and 1. Probability is determined by taking the number of chances of the event and dividing it with the total number of chances. It can be expressed as a per cent or as a ratio. Some investigations use terminology such as 'winning streak' and 'bad luck', which may influence a person's thinking but may have no effect on probability.

Page 15
These pages further explore the concept of probability as investigated on page 13. If an event has a probability of 0 then it cannot happen, while a probability of 1 means it is certain to happen.

As discussed above, probability is determined by taking the number of chances of the event and dividing it with the total number of chances. For example, selecting a blue marble from a bag involves them finding how many blue marbles there are (4) and dividing it by the total number of marbles (12) to get a ratio of 4:12 which can be also written as 1:3.

Possible difficulties
- Confusion over the concepts of chance and probability
- Taking into consideration previous events which are not related to the current event
- Difficulty with the concept of ratio

Extension
- Look at the temperature and number of days of rain for the previous year and explore the probability of rain, sunshine and temperature for your local area.
- Explore the use of vocabulary and how it is used when discussing chance and probability.

WEATHER OR NOT

City	Max temp (°C)	Min. temp (°C)	Rainfall (mm)	Days of rain
Brisbane	35	3.8	2652.4	139
Sydney	38.7	3.5	1499.2	135
Canberra	40.5	– 4.7	562.8	102
Melbourne	41.1	2.2	448.6	130
Hobart	35.2	– 0.4	549.8	140
Adelaide	42.2	1.3	464.6	115
Perth	44.3	3.1	703	110
Darwin	37	12.3	1808.4	143

Australian city summary for temperature and rainfall

1. Which cities have the lowest minimum temperature and the lowest maximum temperature?

_____

2. What is the probability of rain on any day in Sydney?

_____

3. Which city has a mean temperature of 21.75 °C?

_____

4. What is the probability of it not raining in Melbourne?

_____

5. Which city has the largest temperature range?

_____

6. Which cities had a daily average over 8 mm of rain?

_____

7. What is the probability of rain in Hobart?

_____

8. Which three cities have a maximum mean temperature of 40 °C?

_____

9. What is the probability of it being sunny in Perth?

_____

10. Which city had an average of about 4 mm of rain per day?

_____

SHOWTIME

1. Marcy is playing 'Three best throws' in Side Show Alley. She has to throw 3 balls at a circular target which automatically totals the points she gets. If a ball hits the centre she gets 10 points. The middle region scores 5 points and the outside 2 points. What is the probability that she will score 20 points or more?

_____

2. What is the probability she will throw a winning score of 30?

_____

3. Marcy has a winning streak and the next 2 throws she wins a prize. What is the chance her next throw will also win a prize?

_____

4. Krista is playing 'Pick the money card', where she has to pick a card from a set of 7 cards to win some money. Each set of seven cards has two winning cards. She has had 5 tries and has won 2 times. In her next turn what is the likelihood she will pick a money card?

_____

5. Unfortunately, Krista loses her next three turns. What is the chance of her losing 4 times in a row?

_____

6. Rodney works at the hot dog stall from 10:30 to 12:30 each day. The stall sells hot dogs at £3.00 each, 2 for £5.00 or a family set for £8.00. Rodney serves 7 customers in a row who all want hot dogs at 2 for £5.00. What is the probability his next customer will want 2 hot dogs for £5.00?

_____

7. What is the probability he will serve 9 customers in a row who want 2 hot dogs for £5.00?

_____

8. Would he be more likely to sell 9 single hot dogs in a row?

_____

PROBABLY TRUE

1. Georgia is playing cards using a regular pack of 52 cards. How many cards would she need to draw from the pack to be absolutely certain that she has a card with diamonds on it?

_____

2. One bag contains 3 blue dice and 2 yellow dice and another bag contains 2 blue dice and 1 yellow dice. To win a prize Tony needs to select a blue dice from either bag. He can only have one go. Which bag should he choose and why?

_____

3. Andy and Pete are playing with two 10-sided dice with the digits 0–9 on them. When they roll the dice they add the numbers together. What is the probability they will roll a multiple of six?

_____

4. A bag has five blue marbles, three red marbles and four yellow marbles. How many red marbles need to be added to the bag so that the probability of drawing a red marble is $\frac{3}{4}$?

_____

5. A jar contains two yellow marbles, three red marbles and four blue marbles. Carly draws one marble from the jar, and then Toby draws a marble from those remaining. What is the probability that Carly will draw a blue marble and Toby a red marble?

_____

6. June and Shayla have a bag with 5 green counters numbered 1–5. They both pick a counter. June calculates the sum of the numbers while Shayla calculates the product. What is the likelihood that the sum is greater than the product?

_____

7. Kurt is playing with a tetrahedron dice with the digits 1–4 on the four faces. If he rolls the dice twice, what is the probability that the same number will be on the bottom face each time?

_____

Problem-solving

To solve problems involving time and make decisions based on particular criteria

Curriculum links

England (Year 6 progression to Year 7)
- Using and applying: Solve problems by breaking down complex calculations into simpler steps.
- Using and applying: Choose and use operations and calculation strategies appropriate to the numbers and context.
- Measuring: Solve measures problems by calculating.

Northern Ireland (Key Stage 2)
- Processes in maths: Plan and organise their work, learning to work systematically.
- Processes in maths: Develop a range of strategies for problem solving, looking for ways to overcome difficulties.
- Measures: Develop skills in estimation of time.
- Measures: Use the four operations to solve measures problems.
- Measures: Understand the relationship between the 12 and 24-hour clocks.
- Measures: Use timetables.

Scotland (Third)
- +/-/x/÷: Use a variety of methods to solve number problems, clearly communicating my processes and solutions.

Wales (Key Stage 3)
- Skills: Select and use the mathematics, sequences of operation and methods of computation to solve problems.
- Skills: Break complex problems into a series of tasks.
- Skills: Use a range of mental, written and calculator computational strategies.
- Skills: Interpret mathematical information presented in a variety of forms.
- Measures and money: Make sensible estimations of time in everyday situations and less familiar contexts.

Materials

clock

Focus

This page explores reading for information, obtaining information from a number of sources (the plane information, the timetable, the shuttle bus information) and using it to find solutions. The problems involve thinking about and working with time. Decisions about time being too early or too late are needed rather than an exact time.

Discussion

Page 17

Pupils read the information on the page and use it to find a number of solutions. Pupils who are not familiar with 24-hour time can still do the activity using a conversion table. The investigation can be used to explore the concept of 24-hour time. Pupils need to read for information, get information from a number of sources and fit this information against set criteria.

There are a number of flights that fit the criteria, with other flights resulting in the traveller getting to Cradle Mountain either 'too early' or 'too late'. Once a flight has been deemed too late then others that are later still can be automatically excluded. For example, if the Tassie Airlines plane at 15:50 would not get you to Cradle Mountain before dinner then the flight at 16:45 can also be ruled out. No further explorations are needed for these flights.

Similar thinking can be used for the flights that are too early. If catching the Tassie Airlines plane at 8:25 gets you to the campsite too early then all flights prior to this time would also be too early and can be quickly excluded.

Pupils need to think in terms of 24-hour time for the flight information, but the before and after times of 1 pm and 6:30 pm are in 12-hour time. They also need to take into consideration that 1 pm and 6:30 pm are 13:00 and 18:30 respectively.

The information regarding the taxi and the wait time at the airport is needed for investigation 4 to determine what would be the latest time to leave home to go to the airport. Some pupils may try to include this in their travel calculations. The bus leaves the airport every hour starting at 7:20, which means a bus leaves 20 past each hour. However, if the plane arrives at 11:15 they would not be able to catch the 11:20 bus as they need to exit the plane and collect their luggage. Pupils need to consider this time in their solutions.

Possible difficulties

- Unfamiliarity with a timetable
- Confusion with 24-hour time
- Including taxi and wait time information in the travel calculations
- Thinking that an exact flight is needed rather than flights that are neither too early or too late

Extension

- Use the information and timetable with other criteria; for example, if you need to be in Cradle Mountain to meet a friend for a hike before dinner or you want to look around Launceston before heading out to Cradle Mountain.

WILDERNESS EXPLORER

Imagine you have decided to travel from Sydney to Cradle Mountain in Tasmania for a hiking holiday. You need to fly into Launceston and then catch the bus to Cradle Mountain, which takes 2 hours.

Look at the following information and plan your holiday. The campsite has a 1:00 pm check-in time so you want to arrive after 1 pm but before dinner at 6:30 pm.

• • • •••• • • • • • • • • ••• ——hotel to Sydney Airport • •

- waiting time 25 min.
- travel time 35 min.

- wait time at airport 1 hour
- flight time to Launceston 1 hour 35 min.

Cradle Airlines

Departure times	Flight numbers					
	CA23	CA32	CA47	CA51	CA68	CA74
	6:15	7:20	8:45	11:35	14:25	16:45

Tassie Airlines

Departure times	Flight numbers					
	TA23	TA32	TA47	TA51	TA68	TA74
	5:10	6:55	8:25	10:40	14:10	15:50

- Cradle Mountain bus leaves airport every hour starting at 7:20 am
- travel time to campsite 2 hours

1. I can catch the following flights: _____

2. These flights are too early: _____

3. These flights are too late: _____

4. What would be the latest time I can leave home for each possible flight?

_____

5. What flight would you choose to get you to your destination on time and why?

_____

_____

Problem-solving

To use strategic thinking to solve problems

Curriculum links

England (Year 6 progression to Year 7)
- Using and applying: Solve problems by breaking down complex calculations into simpler steps.
- Using and applying: Choose and use operations and calculation strategies appropriate to the numbers and context.
- Using and applying: Represent information or unknown numbers in a problem; for example, in a table.
- Using and applying: Use step-by-step deductions to solve problems involving shapes.
- Knowing and using number facts: Recognise and use multiples, factors and square numbers.

Northern Ireland (Key Stage 2)
- Processes in maths: Plan and organise their work, learning to work systematically.
- Processes in maths: Develop a range of strategies for problem solving, looking for ways to overcome difficulties.
- Processes in maths: Present information and results clearly.
- Processes in maths: Recognise patterns and relationships and make predictions about them.
- Number: Understand and use multiples and factors and the terms prime and square.
- Number: Use the four operations to solve problems.
- Number: Use the four operations to solve problems involving money.
- Measures: Use the four operations to solve measures problems.
- Measures: Calculate perimeter of simple shapes.

Scotland (Third)
- +/-/×/÷: Use a variety of methods to solve number problems, clearly communicating my processes and solutions.
- +/-/×/÷: Recall number facts quickly and use them accurately when making calculations.
- Multiples, factors and primes: Identify common multiples and factors.
- Multiples, factors and primes: Apply understanding of factors to identify when a number is prime.
- Time: Work out how long a journey will take, including the speed travelled or distance covered, using the link between time, speed and distance.

Wales (Key Stage 3)
- Skills: Select and use the mathematics, sequences of operation and methods of computation to solve problems.
- Skills: Break complex problems into a series of tasks.
- Skills: Use a range of mental, written and calculator computational strategies.
- Skills: Interpret mathematical information presented in a variety of forms.
- Number: Use a calculator efficiently.
- Number: Examine features of numbers, including primes.
- Measures and money: Make sensible estimates of time in everyday situations and less familiar contexts.
- Measures and money: Find perimeters of shapes.

Materials

grid paper, counters in several different colours

Focus

These pages explore more complex problems in which the most difficult step is to find a way of coming to terms with what the problem is asking. Using a table or diagram to explore the situation will assist in seeing all the conditions that need to be considered.

Discussion

Page 19
The first problem can be solved using counters on a grid or colouring the squares to see what is happening.

1	2	3	4	5	6	7	8	9	10

The number of possibilities can then be seen directly or patterns can be sought.

Analysis of the patterns shows that the squares represent the factors of the number of the column in which they occur. Determining the factors of each number 1–50 shows that 48 has the most factors or entries in a column. The other questions are solved by considering prime numbers, squares of prime numbers and systematically examining the pairs of factors in each number.

Page 20
For the first problem, consider the distances covered every 15 minutes (a table or list would help). After 15 minutes, Jane would walk 1 km and have 15 km left, while Jenny would ride 3 km and have 13 km left. After 30 minutes, Jane would walk 2 km and have 14 km left, while Jenny would ride 6 km and have 10 km left. After 45 minutes, Jane would walk 3 km and have 13 km left, while Jenny would ride 9 km and have only 7 km left. Jenny would then be home first. Jenny should leave the bicycle after 30 minutes and they would both arrive home together after 150 minutes. (Tables to illustrate this solution are on page 64).

For the second problem, organising the information on to a table will supply a solution. The slower speed requires an additional 10 km, the faster speed covers 15 km too much:

hours	distance @ 10 km/h	distance to park	distance @ 15 km/h	distance to park
1	10	20	15	0
2	20	30	30	15
3	30	40	45	30
4	40	50	60	45
5	50	60	75	60

After 5 hours, the distance is 60 km so 12 km/h would arrive at the exact time. The third problem is done the same way – the required speed is 9.6 km/h for 5 hours.

Page 21
The puzzle scrolls contain a number of different problems all involving strategic thinking to find possible solutions. In most cases pupils will find tables, lists and diagrams are needed to manage the data while exploring the different possibilities. For example, the investigation about bread rolls could involve pupils list the multiples of 60 in a table with the total to make £11 and seeing which is a multiple of 85.

Multiple of £0.60	Look for a multiple of £0.85	Total
£0.60	£10.40	£11.00
£1.20	£9.80	£11.00

Possible difficulties

- Not using a diagram or table to come to terms with the problem conditions
- Unable to see how to connect the time cycled to the distance travelled
- Considering only some aspects of the puzzle scrolls

Extension

- Change the numbers and the scenarios to write other problems based on the puzzle scrolls.
- Use different speeds and times for the problems on page 20.

CHANGING LOCKERS

The local college has exactly 1000 pupils, each of whom has a locker. The lockers are along the passageways and numbered 1–1000. To raise money for local charities, the pupils organised a competition with an entry fee of £1.00.

All 1000 pupils had to run past, opening or shutting locker doors:

- the first pupil opened the door of every locker
- the second pupil closed every locker door with an even number
- the third pupil changed every third locker, closing those that were open and opening those that were closed
- the fourth pupil changed every fourth locker, and so on.

1. The pupil or pupils who could predict ahead of time which lockers would be open would nominate the charity that would receive the £1000.00.

   (a) What would you predict?

   _____

   _____

   (b) Would any lockers remain open after 10 pupils had passed along the rows of lockers?

   _____

   _____

   (c) Which lockers would be open after 50 pupils had changed 50 lockers?

   _____

   _____

   (d) Can you see a pattern for the numbers of the open lockers?

   _____

   _____

   (e) Use your pattern to work out which lockers would be open after all 1000 pupils had run past.

   _____

   _____

   (f) Can you find some lockers that only changed twice?

   _____

   _____

   (g) Can you see a pattern for the numbers on these lockers?

   _____

   _____

   (h) What is the largest number on a locker that changed only twice?

   _____

   _____

CYCLE DAYS

Jane and Jenny rode their bicycles to the bay for a picnic. On the way back, when they were 16 km from home, the front wheel on Jane's bicycle was damaged in a large pothole and could no longer be ridden. In order for them both to get home in good time, they decided to share the walking and bike riding.

1. At first, Jane would walk while Jenny would ride her bicycle. After some time, Jenny would leave her bicycle at the side of the road and continue on foot. When Jane reached the bicycle, she would then ride it home. Jane walks at 4 km per hour and cycles at 10 km per hour, while Jenny walks at 5 km per hour and cycles at 12 km per hour. How long should Jenny ride her bicycle for both of them to arrive home at the same time?

2. When Jane's bicycle was repaired, they decided to go for another bike ride. This time, they would set off separately and meet at the Jetty at midday, then set up their picnic in the park next door. Jenny knew that if she took it easy and rode at 10 km per hour, she would be an hour late, but if she really pushed herself and rode at 15 km per hour, she would arrive an hour early. At what speed should she ride in order to arrive just on time?

3. Jane did not have quite as far to travel so she knew she did not have to ride as hard as Jenny. If she rode at 12 km per hour, she would arrive an hour early, but if she rode at 8 km per hour, she would be an hour late. At what speed should Jane ride to get there at the same time as Jenny?

4. At what time did each girl leave her home?

PUZZLE SCROLLS

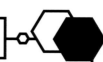

1. £65 000 is divided among 5 brothers with each one getting £3000 more than their younger sibling. How much will the youngest brother get?

2. A rectangular table is twice as long as it is wide. If it was 3 m shorter and 3 m wider it would be a square. What size is the table?

3. How many blocks would you need to make this stack of cubes into a cube 6 blocks high?

4. I spent £11.00 at the bakery buying bread rolls for 60p and 85p. How many of each roll did I buy?

5. How often in a 12-hour period does the sum of the digits on a digital clock equal 9?

6. A triangle has a perimeter of 80 cm. Two of its sides are equal and the third side is 8 cm more than the equal sides.

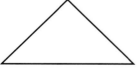

What is the length of the third side?

TEACHER NOTES

Problem-solving

To use spatial visualisation, logical and proportional reasoning and an ability to rename among *fractions and percentages* to solve problems

Curriculum links

England (Year 6 progression to Year 7)
- Using and applying: Solve problems by breaking down complex calculations into simpler steps.
- Using and applying: Choose and use operations and calculation strategies appropriate to the numbers and context.
- Using and applying: Represent information or unknown numbers in a problem; for example, in a table.
- Measuring: Solve measures problems by estimating and calculating.

Northern Ireland (Key Stage 2)
- Processes in maths: Plan and organise their work, learning to work systematically.
- Processes in maths: Develop a range of strategies for problem solving, looking for ways to overcome difficulties.
- Processes in maths: Present information and results clearly.
- Number: Understand and use fractions, decimals and percentages.
- Number: Use the four operations to solve problems involving money.
- Measures: Use the four operations to solve measures problems.

Scotland (Third)
- +/-/x/÷: Use a variety of methods to solve number problems, clearly communicating my processes and solutions.
- +/-/x/÷: Recall number facts quickly and use them accurately when making calculations.
- Fractions, decimals and percentages: Solve problems by carrying out calculations with fractions, decimals and percentages.

Wales (Key Stage 3)
- Skills: Select and use the mathematics, sequences of operation and methods of computation to solve problems.
- Skills: Break complex problems into a series of tasks.
- Skills: Use a range of mental, written and calculator computational strategies.
- Skills: Interpret mathematical information presented in a variety of forms.
- Number: Extend knowledge of number system to include decimals, fractions and percentages.
- Number: Calculate with whole numbers, decimals, fractions and percentages.

Materials

counters, calculator

Focus

These pages explore different ways of visualising the problem situation and analysing the possibilities that make up the whole solution. Logical reasoning is needed, as well as an understanding of measurement concepts of length, perimeter, area and direction. In each situation materials, diagrams or tables can be used to organise, sort and explore the data.

Discussion

Page 23

Using a table to keep track of the times taken in the first problems will enable the different pieces of information to be brought to bear.

The other lift problems can be solved in the same way: leaving from floor 8 they do not arrive at the same time —the fast lift arrives first. From floor 9, the 'slow' lift is quicker—5:22 compared to 5:23.

Time	5:00	5:01	5:02	5:03	5:04	5:05	5:06
Sally	6	5	5	5	5	4	3
Cath	6		5		4	4	4

5:07	5:08	5:09	5:10	5:11	5:12	5:13	5:14	5:15
3	3	3	2	2	2	2	1	
4		3		2		1		

The problem with the passengers on the bus can be solved by 'try and adjust' (the numbers in the problem suggests the number of passengers needs to be a multiple of 5, 2 and 3) or by using the fractions to work backwards. If counters are used to represent the passengers, then adjusted to reflect the fractions involved, it is much easier to see what to do when working backwards.

Page 24

Analysis of the first problem shows that there must be a difference of 600 in the number of copies produced in the time spent copying. Using a 'try and adjust' approach, consider 10 hours (2400 and 2800, a difference of 400), 20 hours (4800 and 5600, a difference of 800), 15 hours (3600 and 4200 – this is a difference of 600). 15 hours were allowed and 400 copies were required.

For the second problem, if 4 copiers take 15 minutes, I copier would take 60 minutes and 3 copiers would take 20 minutes. When another copier jams, the remaining half of the job would take 1 copier 30 minutes, so 2 copiers would take 15 minutes.

The last problem can be solved in the same way as the first, this time considering the number of photos to produce a difference of 8 hours – 2400 photos; 35 hours work was allowed.

Page 25

These problems require seeing how the amounts spent expressed in both percentages and fractions can all be renamed as percentages once the information is untangled. Diagrams both help to sort the information and provide insight into the calculations needed. When the information is placed onto the diagrams, as in the first problem, it is a simple matter to see the value of 1% and thus the separate costs.

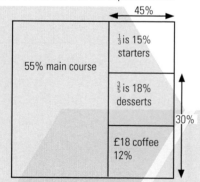

The other problems can be analysed in a similar manner.

Possible difficulties

- Immediately think that the slow lift will get there last
- Unable to construct tables or draw diagrams to show the relationships among floors, copies or hours needed and allocation of money

Extension

- Change the speed of the lifts, the time waiting for passengers and the floor numbers.
- Groups of pupils could write their own problems involving per cents and fractions of money spent on activities and challenge others to solve them.

1. Cath and Sally work on the 6th floor of their office building. When they leave the office to go home at 5:00 pm, Cath gets in the slow lift and Sally gets in the fast lift. The fast lift takes 1 minute between floors and the slow lift takes 2 minutes between floors. The first lift to reach a floor stops for 3 minutes to pick up other office workers on their way home.

(a) Who will be the first to get to the lobby on the first floor?

_____

(b) How long will it take for each of them?

_____

_____

2. Their friends, Kate and Sandra, work in an office two floors above them. They believe it makes no difference what lift they get in.

(a) Are they correct?

_____

_____

(b) What if they worked on the 9th floor?

_____

_____

3. When Cath and Sally left their office building, they caught a bus to the apartment they shared. They noticed an unusual pattern to the way the passengers got on and off the bus:

- At the first stop, $\frac{2}{5}$ of the people got off and $\frac{3}{5}$ of the original number got on.

- At the second stop, $\frac{1}{2}$ of the people got off and $\frac{1}{3}$ of the number that were left on the bus got on.

- When they got off at the next stop, $\frac{3}{4}$ of the people got off and there were only 5 people to continue on their journey.

How many people were on the bus before the girls got on?

_____

_____

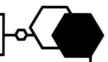

1. Cath and Sally have to produce some documents for a conference coming up in a few days' time. One of the office copiers produces 240 bound copies per hour but would produce 400 copies too few in the time allowed. The other copier produces 280 copies per hour but would produce 200 too many in this time.

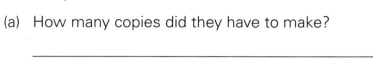

(a) How many copies did they have to make?

_____

_____

(b) What time was allowed to make them?

_____

_____

2. Cath and Sally needed to get the flyers for the conference in today's post. If they used four copiers at the same time, each working at the same rate, it would take 15 minutes to make the number of copies they needed. Unfortunately, one of the machines jammed before they were able to start and it cannot be fixed quickly.

(a) How long will it take the remaining copiers to do the job?

_____

(b) Halfway through the job, another copier jammed. How long would they need to get the remaining flyers printed on 2 copiers?

_____

3. Kate and Sandra have to prepare materials for a big tender due in at the end of the month. They need to scan photos as well as put the finished document into a presentation binder for the courier to collect at 17:00. If they scan 60 photos in an hour, it will take 5 hours more than they have to do the job. If they scan 75 photos in an hour, they will have the job done 3 hours before the deadline.

(a) How many photos do they need to scan?

_____

_____

(b) How many hours work was allowed to complete the task?

_____

OUT OF OFFICE

1. As a reward for getting their work done to such tight schedules, their boss took Cath, Sally, Kate and Sandra out to lunch. After she paid the bill, she noticed that 55% of the cost was for main courses, $\frac{1}{3}$ of the rest was spent on starters, and $\frac{3}{5}$ of the remaining cost went on desserts. If they finished with coffees at £3.60 each, how much did their boss pay for the celebratory meal?

_____

2. After all their hard work, Sally went on holiday. When she returned, she checked her expenses against her budget, as she suspected that rising fuel prices had added quite a bit to her costs. She found that the airfares had increased considerably and accounted for 52% of her spending. The tours and shows she had pre-booked accounted for $\frac{1}{4}$ of the rest of the money she spent. She took the remaining money she budgeted away with her and spent $\frac{3}{4}$ on accommodation and only £450 on meals and shopping.

   (a) How much did she pay for accommodation?

   _____

   (b) What was the cost of her airfare?

   _____

3. Sandra also took some holidays, but she used her time to do some renovations on her townhouse. When she looked at the amounts she had spent, she found that 36% went on the bathroom and $\frac{3}{8}$ of the rest on the kitchen. However, the fittings for these had increased in price and needed $\frac{1}{4}$ of the money remaining after she paid for the kitchen and bathroom. Two thirds of this money went on the patio and $\frac{1}{5}$ on the garden area. Unfortunately, the work cost more than she had anticipated and she overspent her budget by £1720.

   What was the cost of renovating the kitchen, the bathroom and the patio?

   _____

Problem-solving

To use patterns and logical reasoning to determine numbers in spatial arrangements

Curriculum links

England (Year 6 progression to Year 7)
- Using and applying: Solve problems by breaking down complex calculations into simpler steps.
- Using and applying: Choose and use operations and calculation strategies appropriate to the numbers and context.
- Using and applying: Represent information or unknown numbers in a problem; for example, in a formula or equation.
- Using and applying: Generate and describe sequences and use letters to represent unknown numbers.

Northern Ireland (Key Stage 2)
- Processes in maths: Plan and organise their work, learning to work systematically.
- Processes in maths: Develop a range of strategies for problem solving, looking for ways to overcome difficulties.
- Processes in maths: Present information and results clearly.
- Processes in maths: Recognise patterns and relationships and make predictions about them.
- Number: Explore and predict patterns and sequences of whole numbers and follow and devise rules for generating sequences.
- Number: Understand that a letter can stand for an unknown number.

Scotland (Third)
- +/-/x/÷: Use a variety of methods to solve number problems, clearly communicating my processes and solutions.
- +/-/x/÷: Recall number facts quickly and use them accurately when making calculations.
- Mathematicians: Research a famous mathematician and the work they are known for.
- Patterns and relationships: Explore number sequences.

Wales (Key Stage 3)
- Skills: Select and use the mathematics, sequences of operation and methods of computation to solve problems.
- Skills: Break complex problems into a series of tasks.
- Skills: Generalise and explain patterns and relationships.
- Skills: Interpret mathematical information presented in a variety of forms.
- Skills: Interpret and use simple algebraic relationships and functions and predict subsequent terms or patterns in number sequences.
- Skills: Understand algebraic statements.
- Number: Explore number patterns and sequences.
- Algebra: Appreciate the use of letters to represent unknowns.
- Algebra: Generate and generalize simple number sequences.

Materials

counters in two different colours, calculator

Focus

This page explores understanding of numbers in order to discern patterns for triangular numbers and links to the square numbers patterns investigated in Book F. The use of letters to summarise patterns is used to lay a foundation for the thinking used in algebra.

Discussion

Page 27

Pupils should use different coloured counters to explore the pattern shown on the page and extend it to larger numbers in order to describe the relationship between the counters and the triangle. The sum of the first two numbers, 1 + 2 is 3. The sum of the first three numbers, 1 + 2 + 3 is 6. The sum of the first four numbers, 1 + 2 + 3 + 4 is 10 and so on. Two of the same triangular numbers give the corresponding square number and the number, showing a given triangular number is half [number^2 + number]. Pupils should use their counters to investigate how this pattern continues for larger triangular numbers, introducing the use of T_1, T_2, T_3, ... Another pattern that pupils might see is that the triangular number is half [number x (number +1)].

When 2 consecutive triangular numbers are added, they give the square number corresponding to the larger triangular number. This is readily shown with counters for a series of numbers and can be expressed as $T_2 + T_3 = S_3$, $T_3 + T_4 = S_4$ and so on.

This arrangement of numbers in a triangular pattern used by Pascal, in fact first suggested by ancient Chinese mathematicians, is very helpful for summarising relationships in probability (Pascal) and algebra (Ancient China). There are also many interesting patterns that can be discerned among the numbers. The outside diagonals of the triangle consists only of 1, the next diagonal has the counting numbers, and the triangular numbers are in the third diagonal, beginning with 3 (T_2). When the triangular numbers are summed, their sum is diagonally below the last number.

Many other patterns can be investigated as the triangle is extended. Have pupils write out the numbers on a sheet of A4 paper to get as large a triangle as they can. Ask them to highlight the triangular and square numbers in the triangle. Ask them to explore questions such as:

- Is it possible to have a square triangular number?
- Is there a pattern to the location of the square numbers?
- Can they find a way to describe a pattern for the numbers in the other diagonals?

Possible difficulties

- Pupils may find it difficult to accept and use the algebraic form of notation involving T_2 or S_2 etc.
- Unable to see how two triangular numbers form a pattern based on a square number add the number or as a rectangular pattern of the number x [number +1]
- Unable to complete the pattern to give Pascal's triangle

Extension

- Investigate other arrangements of counters to give numbers—these are called Polygonal numbers and extend to pentagonal, hexagonal etc. numbers. Do any of these numbers occur on the Pascal triangle?
- Is it possible to find a relationship between the triangular or square numbers and other polygonal numbers?
- What would happen if this triangular pattern began with the number 2 rather than 1?
- Find some background information about Pascal, a French mathematician who used the patterns on the triangle of numbers that was later named in his honour.
- Investigate the history of this triangle from the times of the Chinese mathematicians and the way it is used currently in mathematics and in applications.

NUMBER PATTERNS

Ancient Greek mathematicians were interested in numbers made from different arrangements of counting objects. Numbers arranged in a triangular pattern suggested the sum of the counting numbers.

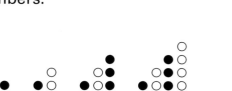

1. Putting 2 of the same triangular numbers gave the corresponding square number + that number; for example:

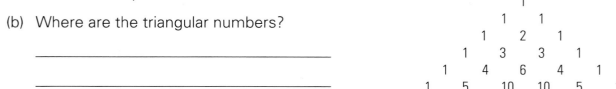

is half $[3^2 + 3]$

(a) The 3rd triangular number, T_3, is half $[3^2 + 3]$.

(b) Is this true for the 4th triangular number, T_4? T_5? T_6? ... _____

(c) What happens when you add a triangular number and the next triangular number?

_____

(d) Show why this is so using a diagram like the one above.

(e) Can you write this pattern using T_1, T_2, T_3, ... for triangular numbers and S_2, S_2, S_3, ... for square numbers?

_____

2. This arrangement of numbers is often called Pascal's triangle: each new entry is formed from the sum of the two numbers above it.

(a) Continue the pattern for several more rows.

(b) Where are the triangular numbers?

_____

_____

(c) Where do you find the sum of the triangular numbers?

_____

```
            1
          1   1
        1   2   1
      1   3   3   1
    1   4   6   4   1
  1   5  10  10   5   1
```

TEACHER NOTES

Problem-solving
To identify and use number understanding

Curriculum links
England (Year 6 progression to Year 7)
- Using and applying: Solve problems by breaking down complex calculations into simpler steps.
- Using and applying: Choose and use operations and calculation strategies appropriate to the numbers and context.

Northern Ireland (Key Stage 2)
- Processes in maths: Plan and organise their work, learning to work systematically.
- Processes in maths: Develop a range of strategies for problem solving, looking for ways to overcome difficulties.
- Processes in maths: Present information and results clearly.

Scotland (Third)
- +/-/x/÷: Use a variety of methods to solve number problems, clearly communicating my processes and solutions.
- +/-/x/÷: Recall number facts quickly and use them accurately when making calculations.

Wales (Key Stage 3)
- Skills: Break complex problems into a series of tasks.
- Skills: Interpret mathematical information presented in a variety of forms.

Materials
calculator

Focus
These pages explore solving problems involving number sense, magic squares and logic. Analysis of the problems to locate given information is necessary to find the magic number or the arrangement of numbers. Counters, blocks or a calculator can be used to assist as these problems focus on the concepts of number sense and number logic rather than basic facts.

Discussion
Page 29
This investigation involves the concept of magic squares. All rows, columns and diagonals in a magic square add to the same total. Four by four magic squares have been used.

Page 30
This page explores the concept of sudoku. The word 'sudoku' roughly means 'digits must only occur once'. In this case 9 by 9 grids have been used so every row, column and mini-grid must contain one of each of the digits 1 – 9. No addition or basic facts are involved and pupils need to use logical reasoning to find solutions.

Page 31
The puzzles on these pages are known as alphametic or cryptorithm puzzles where letters in words are substituted for numbers in an addition algorithm. There are a number of famous alphametic puzzles such as 'send more money' and 'no more cash'. Both of these puzzles have a number of different possibilities that can fit the criteria. In the example provided, you know that the M must be a 1 as you are adding two 4-digit numbers and as such can only result in a 1 in the ten thousands place. As the M and S are different letters, you know that the S must be eight or nine to result in a 5-digit number. Either way means that O must be 0. If you decided to make the S a 9 and look to the hundreds place the two unknown digits must be consecutive as we know that O is zero and as the other letters are different, then a ten must have been renamed to get a different letter when adding zero. At this stage it is possible to use a number of different combinations. We can see that 4 and 5 work as do 5 and 6. Once you select your consecutive numbers and have found E you then have a number in both the tens and the ones place to work around. Pupils can be encouraged to see how many different possibilities there are. Teachers may like to give pupils a number in each puzzle to get started; e.g. the E is 5.

Possible difficulties
- Considering only rows or columns rather than rows, columns and diagonals in magic squares
- Not thinking strategically when doing the sudoku or the alphametic puzzles

Extension
- Investigate other magic squares, magic numbers and alphametic puzzles.
- Explore sudoku games in magazines, newspapers and on the Internet.
- Try writing other alphametic puzzles for the other pupils to do.

Magic squares have numbers that all add to the same total. All rows, columns and diagonals add to the same total.

Complete these magic squares. Remember, all rows, columns and diagonals must add to the same number.

This magic square has a magic number of _____.

30		12	
	48		18
		27	36
24	39		9

21	18		30
16		22	17
	13		23
19		27	

Magic number: _____

24	21		32
19	31		
30		23	26
22		29	

Magic number: _____

	56	53	66
54		60	55
	51	58	
57		63	

Magic number: _____

	39		49
37	48		38
		41	44
40		46	35

Magic number: _____

20		14	
	27		16
26		19	22
18	23		13

Magic number: _____

	86		98
	97	90	
96	81		91
87	92	95	

Magic number: _____

24	21		
19	31	25	20
30		23	
	27		17

Magic number: _____

72		66	82
67	81		68
80		71	
			65

Magic number: _____

22		16	
	28		18
27	14	21	24
		26	15

Magic number: _____

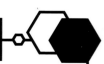

Sudoku puzzles are made up of numbers and to solve them you must use logic to work out where the numbers go.

Every row, column and mini-grid must contain one of each of the numbers 1 to 9.

The completed sudoku has the numbers 1 to 9 in every row, column and mini-grid.

Complete each sudoku using the digits 1 to 9.

5	9	3	4	2	6	8	1	7
1	4	7	8	3	9	6	5	2
8	2	6	5	1	7	4	3	9
7	3	8	1	6	5	9	2	4
9	6	1	2	4	3	5	7	8
4	5	2	9	7	8	3	6	1
6	7	4	3	9	2	1	8	5
2	1	5	6	8	4	7	9	3
3	8	9	7	5	1	2	4	6

Puzzle 1

		2	1			8	3	
8				6				4
4				3		7		1
		8	6	2	5			
			8		3			
			9	1	7	6		
1		9		5				8
6				7				9
	5	7			9	1		

Puzzle 2

8			5		1		3	
	4		7			8	5	
		2						7
1		8		2	3		9	
	7		1	5		6		3
4						9		
	8	6		1		3		
	3		6		4			2

Puzzle 3

		7				3		6
6			4			2	7	
	5	2		1	6		8	
			1		7		3	8
	7	8				5	9	
2	6		8		5			
	2		5	8		1	6	
	3	1			9			7
8		6			4			

Puzzle 4

	6		7		4		8	
		1	6				3	
		3		2	6			
8			5	2	6			7
5								3
4			1	3	8		6	2
6		9	8		1			
	5		2			3	4	
	3				5		9	

Place the digits 1 to 8 in the spaces so that no digit is connected to a consecutive number. That is, 3 cannot connect to 4 or 5.

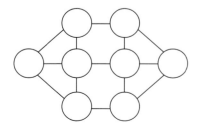

ALPHAMETIC PUZZLES

An alphametic puzzle is an arithmetic problem involving words where there is a one-to-one swapping between letters and digits that makes the arithmetic correct. These puzzles are also called cryptorithms.

On the example below you can see that the phrase 'send more money' can become the arithmetic algorithm.

```
    S   E   N   D            9   5   6   7
    M   O   R   E            1   0   8   5
  ─────────────────        ─────────────────
  M O   N   E   Y          1   0   6   5   2
```

There are many famous and well know alphametic puzzles some of which are listed below for you to solve. All puzzles use addition.

```
        T   E   N
        T   E   N
    F   O   R   T   Y
  ─────────────────────
    S   I   X   T   Y
```

	8	
9		6

```
        D   O
        Y   O   U
    F   E   E   L
  ─────────────────
    L   U   C   K   Y
```

	5	
0		8

```
        I   T
    S   U   I   T   S
            M   Y
  ─────────────────────
    N   E   E   D   S
```

	8	
9		
	3	

```
    I   S   N   T
    T   H   I   S
    F   U   N
  ─────────────────
    S   T   U   F   F
```

9			
	7		
		2	

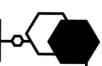

Problem-solving
To analyse and use information in word problems

Curriculum links
England (Year 6 progression to Year 7)
- Using and applying: Solve problems by breaking down complex calculations into simpler steps.
- Using and applying: Choose and use operations and calculation strategies appropriate to the numbers and context.
- Using and applying: Represent information or unknown numbers in a problem; for example, in a table.
- Counting and understanding number: Recognise proportions of a whole and use fractions and percentages to describe and compare them.
- Calculating: Mentally calculate with decimals, fractions and percentages.
- Calculating: Calculate percentage increases or decreases.
- Calculating: Use the memory of a calculator to carry out calculations with more than one step.
- Measuring: Solve measuring problems by estimating and calculating.

Northern Ireland (Key Stage 2)
- Processes in maths: Plan and organise their work, learning to work systematically.
- Processes in maths: Develop a range of strategies for problem solving, looking for ways to overcome difficulties.
- Processes in maths: Present information and results clearly.
- Number: Understand and use fractions, decimals and percentages and explore the relationships between them.
- Number: Use the four operations to solve problems.
- Number: Use the four operations to solve problems involving money.
- Measures: Use the four operations to solve measures problems.

Scotland (Third)
- Estimating and rounding: Round numbers using an appropriate degree of accuracy, taking into account the context of the problem.
- +/-/x/÷: Use a variety of methods to solve number problems, clearly communicating my processes and solutions.
- +/-/x/÷: Recall number facts quickly and use them accurately when making calculations.
- Fractions, decimals and percentages: Solve problems with fractions, decimals and percentages.

Wales (Key Stage 3)
- Skills: Select and use the mathematics, sequences of operation and methods of computation to solve problems.
- Skills: Break complex problems into a series of tasks.
- Skills: Use a range of mental, written and calculator computational strategies.
- Skills: Interpret mathematical information presented in a variety of forms.
- Number: Know about decimals, fractions and percentages and the relationships between them.
- Number: Use a calculator efficiently.
- Number: Calculate with whole numbers, decimals, fractions and percentages.
- Measures and money: Calculate with money and solve problems.

Materials
materials, calculator

Focus
These pages explore word problems that require a number of operations, including division. The wording has been kept fairly simple to help with the problem-solving process. Pupils need to determine what the problem is asking and in many cases carry out more than one step in order to find solutions. Materials can be used to assist with the calculation if necessary as these problems are about reading for information and determining what the problem is asking rather than simply computation or basic facts. See the note on using calculators (page xx) for ways to use the different functions.

Discussion
Page 33
The 'shopping' problems have more than one step with a number of operations and centre around discounts and sale prices. The wording has been kept fairly simple to assist with the problem-solving process. The concept of marked price less discount needs to be explored in order for pupils to come to terms with what the problems are asking. Some problems involve calculating the price after the discount while others involve calculating the full price. A table can be used to assist with the problems involving a set amount and investigating what could be bought for that amount. A calculator can be used to assist if necessary—key in the full amount, press the subtraction key, key in the discount, press the per cent key and the sale price will be displayed.

When exploring what could be bought for £73.50 it is important to keep in mind that DVDs are £12 after the discount and CDs are £18.75. As the total has 50 pence there had to be 2 CDs purchased (4 results in a total that is too much). This reasoning can be used for a number of the investigations where is it important to look at the total and think about what combinations could be used rather than trying combinations at random.

Page 34
In most cases each problem has more than one step and involves multiplication. Some of the investigations involve the concept of profit while other investigations have a number of combinations and pupils can use various ways to solve them. For example, the investigation regarding herb punnets could use a table with the multiples of 4 and 9 to find the various combinations. Pupils could then look for a pattern regarding the multiples.

Multiples of 4	Look for a multiple of 9	Total
4	320	324
8	316	324
...	...	324
32	292	324

Page 35
The 'farm' problems involve the concepts of mass, area and per cent. In most cases more than one step is needed to find a solution. The investigation about ploughing looks at an area of land (12 hectares) and how much has been ploughed each day. The first example could be converted from $\frac{1}{4}$ to 25% which together with the 40% adds to 65% which means the farmer ploughed 35% or 4.2 hectares on the third day.

Some solutions need to be examined in light of the investigation in order to make sense. For example, the investigation about banana plants results in 526.8 plants needing to be replaced. As you would not have 0.8 of a plant, the appropriate solution would be 527 plants each year.

Possible difficulties
- Confusion over the need to carry out more than one step to arrive at a solution
- Using all the numbers listed in the problems rather than just the numbers needed
- Not thinking in terms of the problem and writing solutions such as 763.3 bins
- Difficulty with the concepts of tonnes, discount, per cent, profit

Extension
- Pupils could write their own problems and give them to other pupils to solve.

AT THE SHOPS

1. The music shop has 20% off the marked price for all DVDs and 25% off the marked price for all CDs. I buy 4 DVDs which have a marked price of £15 and 2 DVDs which have a marked price of £12, as well as 6 CDs which have marked price of £25. How much did I pay?

   _____

2. My friend who is shopping with me also buys DVDs which have a marked price of £15 and CDs which have marked price of £25. At the checkout she pays £73.50. What could she have bought?

   _____

3. (a) The computer store has a sale of 20% off all desktop and laptop computers. I buy a printer with a marked price of £149 and a laptop computer with a marked price of £1499. How much did I pay after the sale price had been taken into account?

   _____

   (b) Another customer buys a desktop computer and a colour laser printer for £1435. If the sale price of the printer was £475, what was the marked price of the desktop computer?

   _____

4. (a) The jeans store has T-shirts at £24.99 each or 3 for £60 and jeans for 15% off the marked price of £75. If I spend £187.50, what could I have bought?

   _____

   (b) Another customer who is shopping buys 6 T-shirts and 2 pairs of jeans. How much did he spend?

   _____

5. The shoe store has a sale of 'buy one pair and get the second pair of the same shoes for half price'. I buy one pair of shoes and get the second pair for half price. If I pay £103.50, how much was each pair of shoes?

   _____

THE PLANT NURSERY

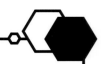

1. During the week the nursery planted 3456 flower punnets and 297 herb punnets. A flower punnet has 9 seedlings, a herb punnet has 4 seedlings and a fern punnet has 6 seedlings. How many seedlings were planted during the week?

_____

2. When getting flowers ready for spring the nursery used punnets which held 4, 6 and 8 seedlings. How many seedlings were planted if 468 medium punnets were used?

_____

3. During October the nursery sold 804 bags of bark chips, which they sell for £35 each. How much money did they make if it cost them £16 per bag?

_____

4. On Friday morning 275 flower punnets were fertilised and 120 herb punnets were watered. During the afternoon another 82 punnets were watered and 68 punnets were fertilised. If there are 6 seedlings in each punnet, how many seedlings were watered?

_____

5. When planting herb seedlings, punnets of 4 and 9 were used. What combination of punnets could be used if 324 seedlings were planted?

_____

6. Over the weekend the nursery made £396 from its fern sale. The punnets sold for 20% off the marked price of £9. How many punnets did they sell?

_____

7. The nursery has 347 fern seedlings to sell which have been planted in punnets of 3 or 8. One table has 30 punnets which hold 180 seedlings and the other table has 34 punnets which hold 167 seedlings. What combination of punnets are on each table?

_____

ON THE FARM

1. A potato grower estimates that the amount of dirt on the brushed potatoes he takes to market is about 2% of their total mass. He gets £240 per tonne for washed potatoes and £220 per tonne for brushed potatoes. If he sells 1.3 tonnes of brushed potatoes, how much is dirt?

_____

_____

2. The cherry farmer knows he will lose about 8% of his crop to birds and about 4% to wastage. If he wants to take about 120 tonnes to market, how many tonnes will he need to start with?

_____

3. The farmer is ploughing 12 hectares of land ready to plant his wheat crop. He ploughs $\frac{1}{4}$ on the first morning, another 40% on the second morning and the rest on the third morning. How many hectares did he plough on the third day?

_____

4. An apple grower estimates that an apple core is about 8% of the mass of an apple. If apples are sold for £3.50 per kilogram, how much are you paying for the core?

_____

_____

5. The banana farmer replaces his plants every 3 years. He has a 3-year cycle and each year he replaces $\frac{1}{3}$ of his plants. He has 8 hectares of bananas and each hectare has 1450 plants. In addition to the planned replacements he knows that about 3% of his plants die and also need replacing. How many new plants does he need each year?

_____

6. The fruit farmer has a 23 hectare property of which 15 hectares is planted with a variety of fruit trees. He has 35% planted with apples, $\frac{1}{4}$ planted with peaches, 12% with apricots and the rest with nectarines. How many hectares does he have for each fruit?

_____

7. During the wheat harvesting season trucks are often used to take the wheat to the storage silo. Each truck can carry 5 tonnes of wheat. How many trips would be needed to transport 2470 tonnes of wheat if 4 trucks were used?

_____

Problem-solving
To use strategic thinking to solve problems

Curriculum links
England (Year 6 progression to Year 7)
- Using and applying: Solve problems by breaking down complex calculations into simpler steps.
- Using and applying: Choose and use operations and calculation strategies appropriate to the numbers and context.
- Using and applying: Represent information or unknown numbers in a problem; for example, in a table.
- Counting and understanding number: Recognise proportions of a whole and use fractions and percentages to describe and compare them.
- Calculating: Mentally calculate with decimals, fractions and percentages.
- Calculating: Calculate percentage increases or decreases.
- Calculating: Use the memory of a calculator to carry out calculations with more than one step.

Northern Ireland (Key Stage 2)
- Processes in maths: Plan and organise their work, learning to work systematically.
- Processes in maths: Develop a range of strategies for problem solving, looking for ways to overcome difficulties.
- Processes in maths: Present information and results clearly.
- Number: Understand and use fractions, decimals and percentages and explore the relationships between them.
- Number: Use the four operations to solve problems.
- Number: Use the four operations to solve problems involving money.

Scotland (Third)
- +/-/x/÷: Use a variety of methods to solve number problems, clearly communicating my processes and solutions.
- +/-/x/÷: Recall number facts quickly and use them accurately when making calculations.
- Fractions, decimals and percentages: Solve problems with fractions, decimals and percentages.

Wales (Key Stage 3)
- Skills: Select and use the mathematics, sequences of operation and methods of computation to solve problems.
- Skills: Break complex problems into a series of tasks.
- Skills: Use a range of mental, written and calculator computational strategies.
- Skills: Interpret mathematical information presented in a variety of forms.
- Number: Know about decimals, fractions and percentages and the relationships between them.
- Number: Use a calculator efficiently.
- Number: Calculate with whole numbers, decimals, fractions and percentages.
- Measures and money: Calculate with money and solve problems.

Materials
calculator

Focus
This page explores problems that require analysis of the connections among the data to determine what needs to be done and whether there is a unique solution. A knowledge of simple percentages is also called on. A process of 'try and adjust' can be used; however, reasoning logically about the possibilities and using a table or diagram to organise them will be more productive. These ways of thinking can then be generalised to other complex problems.

Discussion
Page 37
There are several ways these problems can be solved. Try and adjust: Fix the cost of the crabs and fish at £192 and the cost of the fish and crayfish at £135. Try £150 for crabs, £42 for fish. The crayfish must be £93. This gives too small a cost for the crabs and crayfish (£243 instead of £263). Using a table makes it easier to see how to adjust:

	Crabs	Fish	Crayfish	Crabs and Fish	Fish and Crayfish	Crabs and Crayfish
Try	142	50	85	192	135	227 – too little
Try	150	42	93	192	135	243 – too little
Try	155	37	98	192	135	253 too much
Try	160	32	103	192	135	263

A form of algebraic reasoning is another way. Since the crabs and crayfish cost £263 and the fish and crayfish cost £135, the difference in price between the crabs and the fish must be £128. Since the crabs and fish cost £192, 2 crabs cost £192 + £128 or £320.

The 5 crabs cost £160 or £32 each, a fish costs £32 and the 2 crayfish cost £103 or £51.50 each. The total cost is £295.

The second problem is similar to the first. Mussels £5.75 per kg, 1 kg of scallops costs £27.50.

Possible difficulties
- Not using a table or diagram to manage the data when using 'try and adjust'
- Only keeping one condition in mind when there are two aspects to be considered
- Unable to see how to change the given prices to find sums and differences in order to get the price of two of an item
- Unable to use the forms of algebraic thinking that answer the problems more directly

Extension
- Discuss the various methods used by pupils to solve the problems. Include the ones discussed above. Ask them to solve each problem using a different method from that they used or tried first.
- Encourage pupils to use an algebraic way of thinking about the relationships among the information. Some pupils may be able to express this diagrammatically or with symbols.
- Challenge pupils to change the numbers in the problems so that solutions are still possible.
- Pupils could also write problems using different contexts and larger numbers for others in the class to try.

FISHERMAN'S WHARF

1. Chris bought five crabs, a large fish and two crayfish. If the crabs and the fish cost £192.00, the fish and the crayfish cost £135.00 and the crabs and the crayfish cost £263.00, what was the price of each individual seafood?

   How much did he spend altogether?

   _____

   _____

   _____

   _____

2. (a) Last week, Chris's friend Charlie bought some frozen seafood at the wharf—a tray of whiting, a 5 kg box of half-shell mussels and a 7 kg box of scallops. If the whiting and the mussels cost £85.00, the mussels and the scallops cost £221.25 and the whiting and the scallops cost £248.75, how much did he pay for each seafood?

   _____

   (b) How much do the mussels cost per kg?

   _____

   (c) What is the cost of 1 kg of scallops?

   _____

3. On Wednesday morning, Charlie paid £144.00 for 2 kg of coral trout and 3 kg of reef cod. When Chris went to buy the same fish on Wednesday afternoon, the price of the coral trout was reduced by 10% and the price of the reef cod was reduced by 15%. Chris paid £126.00 for 2 kg of coral trout and 3kg of reef cod. What was the original price of each fish?

   _____

4. The fisherman cut up a fish and sold the head for soup, the body for fillets and the tail as a piece to barbeque. He sold the tail for £4.00, the head for the same price as the tail and half the body, and the body for the same price as the head and the tail. How much did he get for the whole fish?

   _____

Problem-solving

To use spatial visualisation and measurement to solve problems

Curriculum links

England (Year 6 progression to Year 7)
- Using and applying: Solve problems by breaking down complex calculations into simpler steps.
- Using and applying: Choose and use operations and calculation strategies appropriate to the numbers and context.
- Using and applying: Use step-by-step deductions to solve problems involving shapes.
- Knowing and using number facts: Recognise the square roots of perfect squares.

Northern Ireland (Key Stage 2)
- Processes in maths: Plan and organise their work, learning to work systematically.
- Processes in maths: Develop a range of strategies for problem solving, looking for ways to overcome difficulties.
- Processes in maths: Recognise general patterns and relationships and make predictions about them.
- Number: Understand and use the terms square.
- Measures: Develop skills in estimation of area.
- Measures: Use the four operations to solve measures problems.
- Measures: Calculate the perimeters and areas of shapes.

Scotland (Third)
- +/-/x/÷: Use a variety of methods to solve number problems, clearly communicating my processes and solutions.
- +/-/x/÷: Recall number facts quickly and use them accurately when making calculations.
- Measurement: Solve practical problems by applying knowledge of measure and using a formula to calculate area.
- Measurement: Find the area of 2-D shapes, applying knowledge to solve practical problems.

Wales (Key Stage 3)
- Skills: Select and use the mathematics, units of measure, sequences of operation and methods of computation to solve problems.
- Skills: Break complex problems into a series of tasks.
- Skills: Use a range of mental, written and calculator computational strategies.
- Skills: Interpret mathematical information presented in a variety of forms.
- Measures and money: Find perimeters and areas of shapes.

Materials

paper to fold and visualise areas and perimeters, tangram triangles or similar to see the relationships among triangles and squares, calculator

Focus

These pages explore ideas of area and perimeter, using knowledge of squares and triangles to visualise shapes and determine the lengths of sides and areas from which they are composed. Spatial and logical thinking as well as numerical reasoning and organisation are required to investigate the relationships among the shapes to determine distances and areas. See the note on using a calculator (page xx) for ways to use the different functions.

Discussion

Page 39

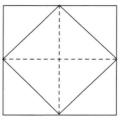

Pupils need to visualise the way in which the squares are reducing each time to be half of the one in which they are embedded. Since the area of the original square is 1600 cm², the next square has an area of 800 cm², the next 400 cm², the next 200 cm² and the red square has an area of 100 cm². Similar thinking about the triangles shows that the 4 coloured triangles must be half of the area of the square they sit in, so that the total red area is 800 + 200 + 100 or 1100 cm².

The black area must be the balance of the area of the original square, 500 cm². The blue area is found by considering the area of the rectangles around the original square. The green area continues the pattern of halving the area, so is 50 cm².

Page 40

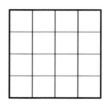

These problems can be solved by thinking of the square in terms of smaller squares corresponding to the number of rectangles. In the first problem, each rectangle is made up of 4 small squares—10 sides of the square make the perimeter of the rectangle.

Each side is 1.5 cm, and the square has a perimeter of 24 cm and an area of 36 cm². Similar reasoning about area and perimeter provides solutions to the other problems.

Page 41

This page extends the thinking about areas. Rather than use complex calculations based on areas of triangles, visualising how the diamond shape can be used to form a larger triangle which is half of a square of side 12 m immediately gives the area of the garden bed as 72 m². Pupils would find it helpful to use triangles to make two of the diamonds and then rearrange them to see they have a large square whose side is the diagonal.

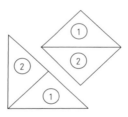

The last problem asks for squares with differences of 99 and 200. Using a calculator or table to systematically check the squares, then add 99 shows that 15² is 225 and 99 more is 324 or 18² but 200 more is 425, which is not a square. Further investigation leads to 49², 50² and 51²; i.e. 2401, 2500, 2601.

Possible difficulties
- Unable to visualise smaller shapes within the larger shapes
- Cannot see how areas and perimeters are formed from those of the smaller shapes
- Unable to visualise how the diamond forms half of a larger square

Extension
- Investigate other aspects of the problems; for example, make further squares in the first quilting pattern, colour the triangles differently and work out the new areas and fractions, try other square or diamonds in which the length of the diagonal is known.
- Have pupils devise other areas within grids as on page 39 and give to one another to solve.

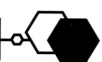

MAKING DESIGNS

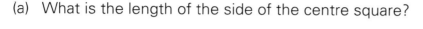

1. A square of side 40 cm was used to make this pattern for a wall hanging by drawing lines from the midpoints of each side to make the nested squares. The artist decided to use red fabric for the centre square.

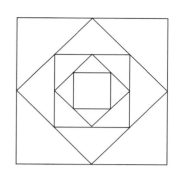

(a) What is the length of the side of the centre square?

_____

(b) What is the area that would be red?

_____

(c) Later, to make the design more striking, he decided to make some of the triangles red as well. What area would be red now?

_____

(d) If black fabric was used for the other triangles, what is the area that is black?

_____

2. When he had finished, he decided to put a blue border around the whole design using fabric that was 5 cm wide.

(a) What is the area of the wall hanging now?

_____

(b) What is the area of the border?

_____

(c) What fraction of the whole wall hanging does the border form?

_____

(d) What fraction of the wall hanging is red?

_____

(e) What fraction is black?

_____

(f) If he made one more square in the centre of the design from green fabric, what would be the area of the green square?

_____

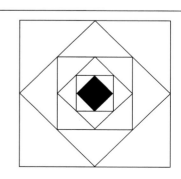

SQUARES AND RECTANGLES

1. A small square is cut into four equal-sized rectangles, each with a perimeter of 15 cm. What is the perimeter and area of the square?

_____

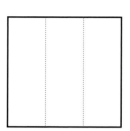

2. A large square is cut into three equal-sized rectangles, each with an area of 192 cm². What is the perimeter of the square and each rectangle?

_____

3. A small square is cut into five equal-sized rectangles, with an area of 9.8 cm². What is the perimeter of each rectangle?

_____

21 m

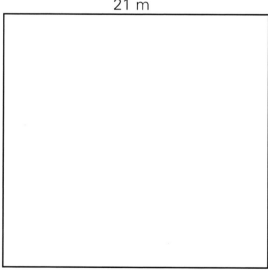

4. (a) A large square with side 21 m is cut into six equal-sized rectangles. What is the perimeter of each rectangle?

_____

(b) If the square was cut into rectangles, each with a perimeter of 45 m, how many rectangles would there be?

_____

5. A square lawn in the centre of a hot city is being replaced with drought-tolerant native grasses. The city has gathered eight different grasses to plant into equal-sized rectangular garden beds, with a narrow border around each bed. If the area planted to each grass is 24.5 m², what is the length of the border around each garden bed?

_____

DESIGNER SQUARES

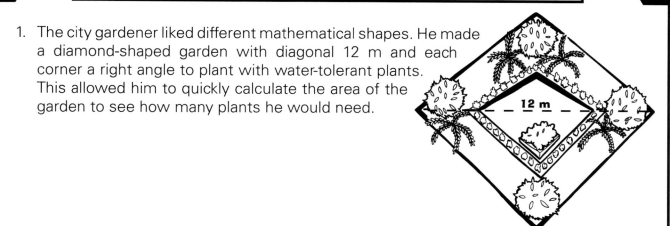

1. The city gardener liked different mathematical shapes. He made a diamond-shaped garden with diagonal 12 m and each corner a right angle to plant with water-tolerant plants. This allowed him to quickly calculate the area of the garden to see how many plants he would need.

   12 m

   What was the area of the garden? (Think about the area of twice the diamond.)

   _____

2. To renovate the central city area, the main piazza was to be paved with square green tiles to form 3 linked large squares. The region around them was to be paved with square yellow tiles of the same size.

   When they drew up their quote for the renovation, Tessellate Tiling Company found that:

   • an exact number of tiles was needed for each large square

   • the medium-sized square had 99 more tiles than the small square

   • the largest square used 200 more tiles than the small square.

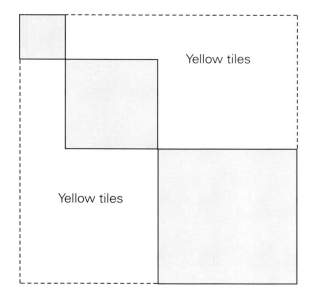

Yellow tiles

Yellow tiles

(a) How many tiles are required for each of the squares?

   _____

   _____

(b) How many yellow tiles are required for the region around them?

   _____

   _____

Problem-solving

To interpret and organise information in series of interrelated statements and to use logical thinking to find solutions

Curriculum links

England (Year 6 progression to Year 7)
- Using and applying: Solve problems by breaking down complex calculations into simpler steps.
- Using and applying: Choose and use operations and calculation strategies appropriate to the numbers and context.
- Measuring: Solve measures problems by estimating and calculating.

Northern Ireland (Key Stage 2)
- Processes in maths: Plan and organise their work, learning to work systematically.
- Processes in maths: Develop a range of strategies for problem solving, looking for ways to overcome difficulties.
- Number: Use the four operations to solve problems involving money.
- Measures: Use the four operations to solve measures problems.

Scotland (Third)
- +/-/x/÷: Use a variety of methods to solve number problems, clearly communicating my processes and solutions.
- +/-/x/÷: Recall number facts quickly and use them accurately when making calculations.
- Time: Work out how long a journey will take, the speed travelled at or distance covered, using knowledge of link between time, speed and distance.
- Measurement: Solve practical problems by applying knowledge of measure.

Wales (Key Stage 3)
- Skills: Select and use the mathematics, units of measure, sequences of operation and methods of computation to solve problems.
- Skills: Break complex problems into a series of tasks.
- Skills: Use a range of mental, written and calculator computational strategies.
- Skills: Interpret mathematical information presented in a variety of forms.
- Measures and money: Make estimates of time in everyday situations, extending to less familiar contexts.
- Measures and money: Calculate with money and solve problems.

Focus

These pages explore the concepts of average, distance, payments and interrelated statements within problem situations. Pupils need to read the problems carefully in order to take into consideration a number of different criteria. Tables and lists can be used to help manage the various criteria.

Discussion

Page 43
Analysis of these investigations reveals a series of interrelated statements which need to be taken into consideration in order to find a solution. A table or list can be very helpful to manage the data. For example in the first investigation, a table listing the different months can be used as a starting point. The problem states how many visitors there were during August and this information can be used to work out the number of visitors in July — 9000 more. That information can in turn be used to work out the numbers for the other months. A similar table or list can be used for the other problems. In the investigation about the Pinnacles, the number of visitors in 2006 is not needed to find a solution. The last problem contains additional information about an increased percentage of visitors which is also not needed to find a solution.

Page 44
These problems explore the concept of average distance travelled over a period of time. In many cases the solution is not necessarily exact but rather an approximate time or distance. For example, the problem about running states that Paula runs 100 m in 'about 50 seconds'. This is not an exact time and would vary from lap to lap so the solution of how far she has run would again be an approximate distance. The investigation about driving from Rome to Venice contains information about a coffee break and lunch that needs to be factored into the amount of time driving. If they leave at 9:15 in the morning, stop for 40 minutes for a coffee break and then have lunch at 12:30 they have driven for 2 hours and 35 minutes not 3 hours and 15 minutes. The problem involving the triathlon deals with the concept of distance over a month. Discussion could centre on how this would vary from month to month. A table could be constructed to show the distance for each month of the year.

Page 45
A careful reading of each problem is needed to determine what the problem is asking as some investigations have information not needed to find a solution. The first investigation requires pupils to calculate how many 250 g packs can be made from 74 kg of cheese and how many 200 g packs can be made from 42 kg of sun-dried tomatoes and to use this to calculate how much profit is made across a month.

In the problem about the shelving and brackets, it is important to keep in mind that each bracket needs six screws which come in packs of 10. Pupils need to calculate how many packets rather than how many screws are required.

When exploring the problem about the tree seedlings, it is important to factor in that he is working on both Saturday and Sunday and thus getting paid at £47.50 per day and not £35.75.

Possible difficulties

- Not using a table or list to manage the data
- Not understanding average
- Confusion when dealing with approximate times and distances

Extension

- Construct a table to show the running distance and how it varies from month to month.
- Write other problems using the same form of complex reasoning for other pupils to solve.

HOW MANY?

1. Around half a million people visit Uluru in Australia each year. Many of these visitors go on to visit the Olgas which has about 200 000 people visit it each year. During August 178 000 tourist visited Uluru while May had twice as many visitors as January but 6000 less than July. July had 9000 more visitors than August. How many visitors were there in January?

_____

2. Around 250 000 people visit the Pinnacles in Nambung National Park in Western Australia each year. Many people visit from August to October when the weather is cooler and the wildflowers are blooming. There were 1 third more visitors in 2008 than in 2004. There were 17 660 more visitors in 2008 than in 2007 and 36 180 less visitors in 2006 than 2007. 2005 and 2004 had similar numbers with only 5 790 more in 2005 than in 2004. If there were 192 980 visitors in 2005, how many were there in 2007?

_____

_____

3. The Blue Mountains west of Sydney experienced declining visitor numbers for several years. An extensive advertising campaign has helped gain an increase in visitors and now about 2.6 million people visit the area each year. Both national and international visitor numbers have improved and 2008 saw an 18% increase in international visitors to the area. Many visitors attend the popular winter magic festival as well as the many other festivals and events held throughout the year. During May there were 196 590 visitors. November had 36 470 more visitors than September and October had 37 210 less than May. May had 73 890 less visitors than July and September has 12 400 less than July. July had 47 480 more visitors than October. How many visitors were there in November?

_____

_____

HOW FAR?

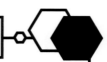

1. Paula runs around a 400 m track on Mondays, Wednesdays and Fridays, and a 200 m track on Tuesdays and Thursdays. She likes to pace herself and averages 100 m in about 50 seconds. She usually runs for an hour on Tuesdays and Thursdays and 40 minutes on the other days. Approximately how far does she run each week?

_____

2. The Indian Pacific train travels from Sydney to Perth via Adelaide twice a week. The trip takes 65 hours and covers a distance of 4352 km one way. Along the way, the train crosses the Nullarbor Plain and has an average speed of 85 km. If the train leaves Sydney at 2:55 pm how far would it have travelled after 13 hours?

_____

_____

3. Davis swims every morning and usually swims 100 m in about 2 minutes and 5 seconds. During the week, he swims at a 100 m pool near his work and on the weekends he swims in a 50 m pool near his house. He swims for about an hour each day. About how far does he swim each week?

_____

4. Rielly and Rita drove from Rome to Venice, a distance of 566 km. They left at 9:15 in the morning and had lunch at 12:30. They stopped for 40 minutes for a mid-morning coffee and an hour and 15 minutes at lunch. They averaged 90 km per hour before lunch and 95 km per hour after lunch. How far had they driven by 3 o'clock in the afternoon?

_____

5. Ranni trains each day for the triathlon. During the week she swims 2 km each morning and does a 4 km run on Tuesday and Thursday afternoons and a 5 km bike ride on Monday, Wednesday and Friday afternoons. On the weekend she does a mini-triathlon where she does a 1 km swim, 2 km bike ride and a 3 km run. How far does she swim, run and cycle each month?

_____

_____

1. Jack's deli sells 74 kg of feta cheese and 42 kg of sun-dried tomatoes each month. He buys the feta cheese in 10 kg containers for £96.50 and the sun-dried tomatoes in 3 kg tins for £37.00. He then re-packs the cheese into 250 g tubs he sells for £4.50 each and the tomatoes into 200 g tubs which he sells for £4.00 each. How much profit does he make each month on feta cheese?

_____

2. Mal pots tree seedlings for the local forestry to plant for forest revegetation. He can be paid by the day or by the number of tree seedlings he pots. He gets paid £1.15 per seedling or £35.75 per day on weekdays and £47.50 per day on the weekends. He can usually pot about 285 seedling per day. If he works Friday to Thursday, which is the best payment option and by how much?

_____

3. Brent bought avocados from the market at 8 for £9 and sold them at his fruit shop for 3 for £5. Over the weekend he made a profit of £65. How many avocados did he sell?

_____

4. The hardware shop sells shelving with brackets and screws and without brackets and screws. Shelving with brackets and screws costs £32.50 per shelf. Shelving without brackets and screws costs £18.00, brackets cost £2.75 each and screws cost 10 for £1.00. Each shelf needs three brackets and each bracket has 6 screws. If Aaron wants to put up 3 shelves, which is the cheaper option and by how much?

_____

_____

5. Beau has 20 cabins he rents to holiday-makers. He bought some new sheets for the cabins and paid £304 for sheets that cost £19 each. The next day he saw the same sheets for £16 so he bought twice as many as the day before. How much did he spend on sheets?

_____

Problem-solving
To use logical reasoning and an ability to visualise a sequence of events so as to use number patterns to solve problems

Curriculum links
England (Year 6 progression to Year 7)
- Using and applying: Solve problems by breaking down complex calculations into simpler steps.
- Using and applying: Choose and use operations and calculation strategies appropriate to the numbers and context.
- Using and applying: Generate sequences and describe the general term.

Northern Ireland (Key Stage 2)
- Processes in maths: Plan and organise their work, learning to work systematically.
- Processes in maths: Develop a range of strategies for problem solving, looking for ways to overcome difficulties.
- Number: Interpret and use simple relationships expressed in numerical and practical situations.

Scotland (Third)
- +/-/x/÷: Use a variety of methods to solve number problems, clearly communicating my processes and solutions.
- +/-/x/÷: Recall number facts quickly and use them accurately when making calculations.

Wales (Key Stage 3)
- Skills: Select and use the mathematics, sequences of operation and methods of computation to solve problems.
- Skills: Break complex problems into a series of tasks.
- Skills: Use a range of mental, written and calculator computational strategies.
- Skills: Interpret mathematical information presented in a variety of forms.
- Algebra: Develop ideas of algebra and generate simple number sequences.

Materials
calculator

Focus
This page explores problems with large amount of data that needs both computation and patterning to determine solutions.

Discussion
Page 47
These problems can be used to highlight the power of the Analyse–Explore–Try model of problem-solving that has evolved over the varied number, spatial and measurement situations posed in Book G. This is discussed in detail in the introduction. In these problems, the information needs to be carefully analysed to determine the number of eggs that are set out for the race and the distance to run to pick up and return the eggs to the basket, collecting two eggs at a time. Pupils may use counters or a diagram to represent the race and see what is happening.

	1 m		1 m		1 m	
start		egg 1		egg 2		egg 3

When the problem is understood, a table that keeps track of the distances run, the number of times a runner goes from the basket to the eggs and back (50), and the cumulative distance covered would enable an answer to be obtained. A pattern may also be seen in the results.

Egg collected	Distance run	total distance (metres)	
1 & 2	4	4	4
3 & 4	8	4 + 8	12
5 & 6	12	4 + 8 + 12	24
7 & 8	16	4 + 8 + 12 + 16	40
9 & 10	20	4 + 8 + 12 + 16 + 20	60

This would suggest adding all the numbers using a calculator which would give the correct answer of 5100 m or more than 5 kilometres, which at first seems surprising.

Another way is to look for a pattern: 4, 4(1 + 2), 4(1 + 2 + 3), 4(1 + 2 + 3 + 4), …

The total must be 4 x the sum of all the numbers 1 – 50. This result can be found by a very famous method supposedly first shown by the mathematician Karl Gauss when only a young boy.

Sum wanted is $\quad$ 1 + 2 + 3 + 4 + 5 … + 50

This sum is also $\quad$ 50 + 49 + 48 + … + 1

Twice the sum must be 50 x 51 or 2550 so the sum is half of 50 x 51 or 1275.

The winner must run 4 x 1275 m half this sum or 5100 m.

When the same thinking is applied to the second problem, it is quickly seen that each distance run will halve, 2 + 4 + 6 + 8 + … , but so would the length of the race if the number of eggs remained the same (500 m and 25 times to run to and from the basket). The distance would be 2 x half (25 x 26) or 650 m—barely 1 eighth of the original.

The third problem also uses the same thinking—picking the eggs up 3 at a time with a distance of 60 m means that there will be 20 distances to run to the eggs and back to the basket.

Possible difficulties
- Not seeing the way in which the eggs are distributed from the starting line
- Only using the distances to the eggs and not including the distances back to the start

Extension
- Use smaller or larger number of eggs for the race and vary the distance between eggs.
- Ask pupils to research the mathematician Karl Gauss and his famous solution.

PROSPECT PLAINS

1. At the Prospect Plains Easter Festival, the egg gathering competition was always a very popular event. Coloured eggs were set out along the lawn at 1 m intervals. Contestants had to start from a line 1 m before the first egg and collect the eggs, two at a time, placing them in a basket at the starting line before running to get the next 2 eggs.

    The eggs had to be collected in order first and second, third and fourth, fifth and sixth, and so on until the last egg, 100 m from the starting line. The winner was the first person to place all their eggs in their basket.

    (a) How far did the winner have to run?

    _____

    _____

    (b) The race took quite a long time, so one of the organisers suggested halving the distance between the eggs as this would halve the distance competitors had to run. Was he correct?

    _____

    _____

    (c) There was also a children's race where the distance between the eggs was increased to 2 m. The last egg was 60 m from the start and the children were allowed to gather 3 eggs at a time. How far did the winning child have to run?

    _____

    _____

Problem-solving

To organise data and use number understanding to solve problems

Curriculum links

England (Year 6 progression to Year 7)
- Using and applying: Solve problems by breaking down complex calculations into simpler steps.
- Using and applying: Choose and use operations and calculation strategies appropriate to the numbers and context.
- Measuring: Solve measures problems by estimating and calculating.

Northern Ireland (Key Stage 2)
- Processes in maths: Plan and organise their work, learning to work systematically.
- Processes in maths: Develop a range of strategies for problem solving, looking for ways to overcome difficulties.
- Number: Use the four operations to solve problems involving money.
- Measures: Use the four operations to solve measures problems.
- Measures: Calculate area of shapes.

Scotland (Third)
- +/-/x/÷: Use a variety of methods to solve number problems, clearly communicating my processes and solutions.
- +/-/x/÷: Recall number facts quickly and use them accurately when making calculations.
- Time: Work out how long a journey will take, the speed travelled at or distance covered, using knowledge of link between time, speed and distance.
- Measurement: Solve practical problems by applying knowledge of measure.

Wales (Key Stage 3)
- Skills: Select and use the mathematics, units of measure, sequences of operation and methods of computation to solve problems.
- Skills: Break complex problems into a series of tasks.
- Skills: Use a range of mental, written and calculator computational strategies.
- Skills: Interpret mathematical information presented in a variety of forms.
- Measures and money: Make estimates of time in everyday situations, extending to less familiar contexts.
- Measures and money: Calculate with money and solve problems.

Materials

calculator

Focus

These pages explore problems that call on an ability to carefully analyse the relationships among the data and organise the information gained to keep track of the possibilities. Putting the various interrelated aspects into a table or diagram provides a systematic way of dealing with the overlapping conditions. See the note on calculator use (page xx) for ways to use the different functions.

Discussion

Amount	£220		£200	£150
	Mother	Son	Mother + daughter	Son + daughter
Try	£120	£100	£80	£180 – too much
Try	£130	£90	£70	£160 – too much
Try	£140	£80	£60	£140 – too little
Try	£135	£85	£65	£150 – correct

Page 49

The first problem can be solved by 'try and adjust' using a table to keep track of the information:

A form of algebraic reasoning can also be used: Subtracting the amount the son and daughter spent from the amount the mother and daughter spent shows the difference between what the mother and son spent is £50. Adding this to the amount the mother and son spent shows that 2 times what the mother spent is £270. Mother spent £135, son spent £85 and daughter spent £65.

Working backwards solves the second problem but the total distributed has to be kept in mind to work out the shares. Desney receives £90 which is 2 thirds what was left after Carol received £9 and 1 third, so Carol got £54. At this point, £144 has been distributed and this is 2 thirds what was left after Brian received £4 and 1 third, so Brian got £76 and Aunt Alice gave them £220.

The third problem is best solved using a diagram to see that after the £3000 is removed, 1 half or £45 000 goes to the daughter, 2 thirds of what remains or £30 000 to the grandson and the remainder of £15 000 is split equally among the 3 great grandchildren who get £5000 each.

Page 50

The first 3 problems on the page can be solved in a similar manner by drawing up tables to see how the points are allocated and choosing the results that match all conditions. For the last problem, adding the attendances gives 2 times the number who went to the first 3 sessions. Session 4 must have had (118 – half of 194) or 21 attendees.

Page 51

The puzzle scrolls contain a number of different problems all involving strategic thinking to find possible solutions. In many cases pupils will find that tables, lists and diagrams are needed to manage the data while exploring the different possibilities. In some cases where there are infinite answers, the 'smallest number possible' has been added to limit the solutions.

Possible difficulties

- Trying to manage the data without using a table or diagram
- Not considering all aspects and information in the puzzle scrolls

Extension

- Challenge pupils to work out how many people went to each of recording sessions 1, 2 and 3 of the televised quiz show.
- Change the numbers and scenarios to write other problems based on the puzzle scrolls.

MONEY MATTERS

1. A mother, her son and daughter went shopping for presents for Christmas. The mother and son spent £220 on a present for the daughter, the son and daughter spent £150 on a present for their mother, and the mother and daughter spent £200 on the son.

   How much did each of them spend?

   _____

   _____

2. Aunt Alice promised her nephew Brian and nieces Carol and Desney some money to share to help them with their holiday expenses. In order to get the sum, they first had to work out the amount they would share from the way she planned to distribute the money:

   • Brian was to get £4.00 for a milkshake and 1 third of what was left

   • Carol was to get £9.00 for coffee and cake for her and Desney and 1 third of what was left

   • Desney would get the remaining £90.00

   (a) How much money would Brian and Carol get?

   _____

   (b) How much money did their Aunt have to give them altogether?

   _____

3. Great Grandma Jean left £93 000 in her will. She asked that it be shared out so that each of her three great grandchildren received the same amount, their father (her grandson) twice as much as the three great grandchildren together, and to her daughter (the children's grandmother) £3000 more than the father and great grandchildren together. How much does each get?

   _____

   _____

T.V. CASH PRIZE

1. In a television quiz programme, each participant is given 10 questions to answer. Five points are won when a question is answered correctly and 3 points are lost for a question that is not answered correctly or not answered at all.

   (a) How many questions must be answered correctly to score 34 points?

   _____

   (b) What are all the possible scores for the quiz?

   _____

   (c) Because there weren't many different scores for the people in the quiz, the rules were altered so that 3 points were given for a correct answer, 1 point was lost for each incorrect answer and no points were given or lost for a question that was not answered at all. If there were 20 questions and a contestant scored 48, how many answers were correct and how many were not answered?

   _____

   (d) A new quiz show opened up with a more attractive format. Each question that a participant answered correctly led to a prize of £250. A question that was not answered drew a penalty of £500. At the end of the competition, one contestant had answered 7 times more questions correctly than incorrectly and received £3750. How many questions were not answered correctly?

   _____

   (e) The new quiz format made an interesting live event and a total of 118 people attended recording sessions for the first four shows. Seventy people attended both the first two shows, 65 were present for both the first and third shows, and 59 people came to both the second and third shows.

   How many people attended the fourth session?

   _____

PUZZLE SCROLLS

1. Rhyl and Ryan race to the top of 80 stairs. Rhyl gives Ryan a 15 step start. Ryan covers 2 steps at a time and Rhyl 3 steps at a time. Who will reach the top first?

2. Two cars are driving around a 2 km track. One car makes a lap every 70 seconds and the other car every 60 seconds. How long will it take the faster car to be one lap ahead?

3. A farmer counted his cows. If he counted by 7 there were none left over but with 2, 3, 4, 5 or 6 there was always 1 left over. What is the smallest number of cows in the herd?

4. The serial number of my phone is a 4 digit number less than 5000 and uses the digits 3, 4, 6 and 9. The 4 is next the 9, the 3 is not next to the 4 and the 6 is not next to the 3. What is the number?

5. Draw two squares in the diagram so that all the stars are separated.

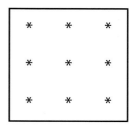

6. Find the area of the shaded parts.

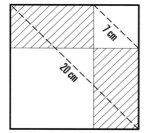

Problem-solving
To use logical reasoning, fractions and measurement to solve problems

Curriculum links
England (Year 6 progression to Year 7)
- Using and applying: Solve problems by breaking down complex calculations into simpler steps.
- Using and applying: Choose and use operations and calculation strategies appropriate to the numbers and context.
- Measuring: Solve measures problems by estimating and calculating.

Northern Ireland (Key Stage 2)
- Processes in maths: Plan and organise their work, learning to work systematically.
- Processes in maths: Develop a range of strategies for problem solving, looking for ways to overcome difficulties.
- Number: Use the four operations to solve problems involving money.
- Measures: Use the four operations to solve measures problems.

Scotland (Third)
- +/-/×/÷: Use a variety of methods to solve number problems, clearly communicating my processes and solutions.
- +/-/×/÷: Recall number facts quickly and use them accurately when making calculations.
- Time: Work out how long a journey will take, the speed travelled at or distance covered, using knowledge of link between time, speed and distance.
- Measurement: Solve practical problems by applying knowledge of measure.

Wales (Key Stage 3)
- Skills: Select and use the mathematics, units of measure, sequences of operation and methods of computation to solve problems.
- Skills: Break complex problems into a series of tasks.
- Skills: Use a range of mental, written and calculator computational strategies.
- Skills: Interpret mathematical information presented in a variety of forms.
- Measures and money: Make estimates of time in everyday situations, extending to less familiar contexts.
- Measures and money: Calculate with money and solve problems.

Materials
paper to draw diagrams or tables and record times, calculator

Focus
The first two pages investigate relationships among distance and time expressed as fractions of the distance around a cycling track. Logical thinking and organisation are needed to see how the cyclists progress, keep track of their positions and determine when they will coincide.

Discussion
Page 53
In the first problem, Gary is halfway around the track and cycles 600 m in 1 minute. Geoff is 1 third the way around the track and cycles 400 m in 1 minute. Exploring how far each rider has cycled after 1, 2, 3 … minutes shows that both cyclists are at the start after 6, 12, 18, … minutes. Another way is to see that Gary reaches the start every 2 minutes, Geoff every 3 minutes –

6, 12, 18 … are common multiples of 2 and 3. Since they cross the start together every 6 minutes, there will be 7 more times as well as the time they started to give 8 times at the start altogether.

Analysing the second problem shows that Gary rides $\frac{24}{56}$ or $\frac{1}{7}$ of the distance around the track before they meet. Geoff must have cycled $\frac{4}{7}$ of the distance in 24 seconds. He would take 6 seconds to travel $\frac{1}{7}$ of the distance and 42 seconds to complete one lap. Put this information into a table:

Time in seconds	24	48	72	96	120	164	168
Geoff	$\frac{3}{7}$	$\frac{6}{7}$	$\frac{9}{7}$	$\frac{12}{7}$	$\frac{15}{7}$	$\frac{18}{7}$	$\frac{21}{7}$ – 3 laps
Gary	$\frac{4}{7}$	$\frac{8}{7}$	$\frac{12}{7}$	$\frac{16}{7}$	$\frac{20}{7}$	$\frac{24}{7}$	$\frac{28}{7}$ – 4 laps

Gary is 1 lap ahead after 2 minutes 48 seconds. When Gary has completed 60 laps, Geoff has only completed 45 laps and has 15 more to ride. Similar reasoning solves the last problem.

Page 54
The first problem is solved the same way as on the preceding page, only the fractions involved are now $\frac{4}{9}, \frac{8}{9}, \frac{12}{9}$ … and $\frac{5}{9}, \frac{10}{9}, \frac{15}{9}$ … .The second problem can be solved by placing some of the information in a table to see the pattern (98 entries is too many!) or else use the different intervals of 4, 5, 2 and 3 days to get a common multiple of 60. They will only ride together one more time on a Wednesday. Similar reasoning shows that Georgia and Gina ride together every 20 days—another 4 times on a Friday, Thursday, Wednesday and Tuesday and the original Saturday.

Page 55
The puzzle scrolls contain a number of different problems all involving strategic thinking to find possible solutions. In most cases pupils will find diagrams, lists and tables are needed to manage the data while exploring the different possibilities. Concepts of space and measurement as well as number are explored and pupils may use a number of different ways to find possible solutions including the 'try and adjust' strategy.

Possible difficulties
- Not able to visualise the distance each person cycles or the time he takes
- Does not use a diagram or table to keep track of the various conditions
- Unable to work confidently with fractions
- Trying to manage the data without using a table or list
- Not considering all aspects and information in the puzzle scrolls

Extension
- Change the times for cycling one lap and passing to give different fractions.
- Change the frequency of the days they rode on the cycle track.
- Change the numbers and scenarios to write other problems based on the puzzle scrolls.
- Challenge pupils to come up with similar problems of their own.

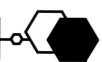

RIDING TO WORK

Due to the high cost of petrol, Gary and Geoff decided to cycle to work rather than drive their cars. However, on the first week they realised they needed to be a lot fitter to ride fast enough to get through the traffic. They used the 1200 m cycle track at the local sports ground for some training. In one minute, Gary rode halfway around the track while Geoff rode $\frac{1}{3}$ of the way.

1. If they both continued to ride at the same speed until they crossed the starting line together, how far will each have cycled?

_____

2. Heavy rain stopped their training after 45 minutes. How many times would they have been at the starting line together?

_____

3. To vary their practice, Gary and Geoff went to another cycle track and decided that they would start at the same point but ride in opposite directions. Geoff was able to cycle around the track in 56 seconds and they pass each other every 24 seconds.

   (a) How many seconds does it take Gary to cycle around the track?

   _____

   (b) When would they next meet at the starting point?

   _____

   (c) How many laps of the track has each rider made?

   _____

4. They decided that each of them would ride 60 laps. When Gary had finished, how many more laps did Geoff need to cycle?

   _____

5. After some additional training, Geoff found he could cycle one lap in 35 seconds while Gary still took 42 seconds.

   (a) How long would it take him to be one lap ahead of Gary?

   _____

   (b) How many laps would he be ahead if they continued cycling at these speeds for one hour?

   _____

Their friends Georgia and Gina also decided to cycle to work and joined Geoff and Gary in training. They liked the idea of cycling around a track in opposite directions so they could see how each other was going. When they first started out, Gina cycled around in 72 seconds and they passed each other every 40 seconds.

1. How many seconds does it take Georgia to cycle around the track?

_____

2. When would they next meet at the starting point?

_____

3. How many laps of the track has each rider made?

_____

4. They decided that each of them would ride 30 laps. When Gina had finished, how many more laps did Georgia need to cycle?

_____

Over the summer when the days were longer, all four cyclists planned to ride along the cycle path by the river after work. Gina decided to ride one night and then take a three-day break. Georgia had four days off between her rides, Geoff cycled every second day and Gary every third day. On the first Saturday evening of summer, they were all at the track together.

5. When will they next be able to cycle together?

_____

6. If there were 14 weeks of summer, how many times would they all cycle together?

_____

7. What days of the week would they be?

_____

8. When would Georgia and Gina ride together?

_____

9. When would Gary and Gina ride together?

_____

10. When would Geoff and Georgia ride together?

_____

PUZZLE SCROLLS

1. Tom bought 69.5m of rope but the metre rule used to measure the rope was 2 cm too long. How much rope did he really get?

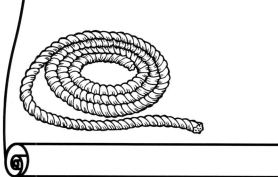

2. The Go-karts company makes number plates with 3 digits followed by one letter. How many different number plates can the company produce?

3. Use the digits 7 to 14 so that each line has a total of 30.

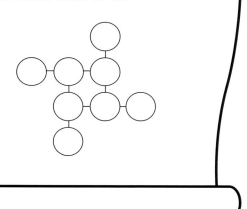

4. A length of rope is cut in half and one piece is used. One third of the other half is cut off and used. If there is 14 m left, how long was the rope to begin with?

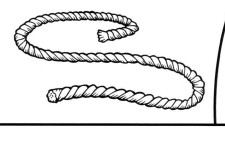

5. Jack and John were paid £135 to fence the paddock. Jack started at 7.00 am and John started at 10.00 am. They finished at 1.00 pm. How much is John's share of the money?

6. A farmer used 368 m of fencing to fence a paddock that is 39 m longer than it is wide. How long and wide is the paddock?

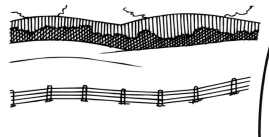

TEACHER NOTES

Problem-solving

To analyse information and use proportional and logical reasoning to solve problems

Curriculum links

England (Year 6 progression to Year 7)
- Using and applying: Solve problems by breaking down complex calculations into simpler steps.
- Using and applying: Choose and use operations and calculation strategies appropriate to the numbers and context.
- Measuring: Solve measures problems by estimating and calculating.
- Handling data: Interpret data and diagrams that represent data.

Northern Ireland (Key Stage 2)
- Processes in maths: Plan and organise their work, learning to work systematically.
- Processes in maths: Develop a range of strategies for problem solving, looking for ways to overcome difficulties.
- Measures: Use the four operations to solve measures problems.
- Handling data: Interpret diagrams.

Scotland (Third)
- +/-/x/÷: Use a variety of methods to solve number problems, clearly communicating my processes and solutions.
- +/-/x/÷: Recall number facts quickly and use them accurately when making calculations.
- Measurement: Solve practical problems by applying knowledge of measure.

Wales (Key Stage 3)
- Skills: Select and use the mathematics, units of measure, sequences of operation and methods of computation to solve problems.
- Skills: Break complex problems into a series of tasks.
- Skills: Use a range of mental, written and calculator computational strategies.
- Skills: Interpret mathematical information presented in a variety of forms.
- Measures and money: Make estimates of time in everyday situations, extending to less familiar contexts.
- Handling data: Interpret information in diagrams.

Materials

calculator

Focus

These pages explore problems that call on an ability to analyse carefully the relationships among the several different items of data and use an understanding of proportional reasoning and numbers to organise the information gained to keep track of the possible answers. The last page introduces the idea of putting the various interrelated aspects into a diagram that allows all the overlapping conditions to be visualised and dealt with in a

systematic way. See the note on calculator use (page xx) for ways to use the different functions.

Discussion

Page 57
These problems require a careful analysis of all of the information presented as well as a sense of proportion to see that the first task would take more time while the second and third tasks would need less time. While a week has seven days, a working week varies according to the type of work and the expectations of the workers. In the first problem, each of the 4 workers works for 15 days. This means the job requires 4 x 15 or 60 days work. If only 3 workers were available, each would work for 20 days and the job would take 4 weeks. Some pupils may also be able to reason that when a team of 4 workers is replaced by a team of 2 workers, this would take twice the time to give 30 days. Counters or base 10 materials could also be used in an array to show how 4 by 15 can be rearranged as 3 by 20.

Page 58
Putting the information for the first problem in a table to show how much water is left after each hour reveals that at 17:00 both dams have 192 m³. There would be 1176 m³ in the pond. The other two problems are best solved using a diagram to show the information:

20 x 20 is 400 fish

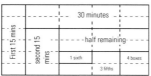

15 x 4 is 60 boxes
(60 – 4) boxes of 25 fish
(1400 fish)

Page 59
This problem involves a large amount of overlapping data that needs to be sorted. A Venn diagram as shown on the page was devised to solve this form of logic problem. The statements need to be read carefully to see where the numbers are placed so that the answers can be identified. The last condition that 85 meals did not have calamari means that 100 meals did have calamari is the key to completing all the entries.

Possible difficulties

- Not seeing how proportion applies to the problems on page 57
- Working with the numbers in the problem rather than the differences on page 58
- Unable to sort out the layers of overlapping information on page 59

Extension

- Seek out other problems using Venn diagrams on the Internet.
- Have pupils investigate the history of logic problems and the work of John Venn and Lewis Carroll (the mathematician author of *Alice in Wonderland*).

FARM WORK

1. A gang of workers is employed to do some repairs around the farm. Four of the workers complete half of one job in 15 days. How many days will it take the full team of ten workers to complete the remaining half of the job? (All workers work at the same rate.)

   _____

2. There were only eight workers to build a stone wall and it took them 6 days. How long would it have taken to build the wall if there had been four more workers when they started the job? (All workers could work at the same rate.)

   _____

3. One of the workers is very skilled and takes 3 days to cut a quantity of fence posts. The other two workers need 4 days to do the same job. How long would it take all of them working together to cut the same quantity of fence posts? (All workers work at the same rate as before.)

   _____

4. Some of the workers are also needed to repair the shearing shed. The work they are doing needs to be done in a certain number of days to meet the deadline for shearing to begin. If there were 3 fewer workers, they would not finish until 6 days after the deadline. If there were 2 more workers, they would finish the work 2 days before the deadline. How many workers are needed to complete the work just on time? How long would the work take them to complete?

   _____

5. It usually takes 3 minutes to fill the trough of water for the cows. However, it has developed a leak that empties it in 4 minutes. How long will it take to fill the trough now?

   _____

FARM PRODUCE

1. One dam on the farm held 720 m³ of water and another held 840 m³. The farmer wanted to pump water from each dam to a pond in which she would grow catfish. At 6:00 she began to pump water from the first dam at a rate of 48 m³ per hour. At 8:00 she started to pump water from the second dam at 72 m³ per hour.

(a) At what time would there be an equal amount of water left in each dam?

_____

(b) How much water would be in the catfish pond at that time?

_____

2. When she had her first crop of catfish, the farmer took them to sell at the wholesale fish market. Fresh Fish Supplies bought 1 quarter of her fish and she sold 2 fifths of the remaining fish to Frozen Fish Sales. After a while, a large Vietnamese Restaurant took 2 thirds of the fish that were left. A family from the city then bought 1 sixth of the remaining fish and, for her final sale, the local fish and chip shop bought 3 fifths of the fish that she still had. As she drove back to the farm with the 20 catfish that had not sold, she felt very happy with her new enterprise and looked forward to her own fish dinner. How many fish did she have to sell?

_____

3. As her catfish multiplied in the pond, she was able to take more fish to market and decided to pack them in boxes of 25 fish. One fifth of the boxes sold in the first 15 minutes, 1 third of what remained in the next 30 minutes, and 1 quarter of what was left in the next 15 minutes. In the next hour, she first sold half of the remaining fish, then 1 sixth of what was left before taking 3 fifths of the remainder to the fish and chip shop and giving the last 4 boxes to the charity kitchen. How many fish did she sell?

_____

_____

SELLING FISH

People from the town and country flocked to the fish and chip shop that stocked the fresh, farmed catfish. Sunday night was especially popular as there was quite a choice of things to have and it meant no-one had to cook dinner.

At the fish and chip shop, all meals come with chips and potato scallops, but customers can choose to have one or more of catfish, calamari rings and battered prawns. Last Sunday, 185 meals were sold between 6.00 and 8.00 pm.

- Forty-five of the meals did not have catfish.
- One hundred and seventy of the meals had catfish or prawns.
- Twenty-five of the meals had calamari, catfish and prawns.
- Sixty meals had calamari and catfish.
- Forty-five meals had catfish and prawns.
- Eighty-five meals did not have calamari.

1. Use this diagram to show how many people ordered each of the different types of meals.

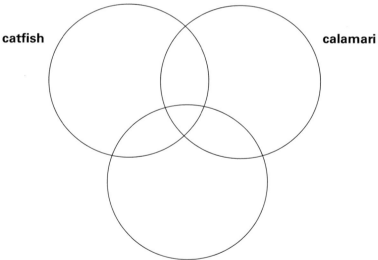

catfish

calamari

prawns

This is a Venn diagram introduced to solve complex logical problems of this form by the mathematician John Venn in the 19th century.

2. How many meals had calamari or prawns?   _____

3. How many meals had prawns only?   _____

4. How many meals had catfish?   _____

5. How many meals had prawns or calamari only?   _____

Problem-solving

To use logical reasoning and measurement to solve problems

Curriculum links

England (Year 6 progression to Year 7)
- Using and applying: Solve problems by breaking down complex calculations into simpler steps.
- Using and applying: Choose and use operations and calculation strategies appropriate to the numbers and context.
- Measuring: Solve measures problems by estimating and calculating.

Northern Ireland (Key Stage 2)
- Processes in maths: Plan and organise their work, learning to work systematically.
- Processes in maths: Develop a range of strategies for problem solving, looking for ways to overcome difficulties.
- Measures: Use the four operations to solve measures problems.
- Shape and space: Understand clockwise and anti-clockwise.

Scotland (Third)
- +/-/x/÷: Use a variety of methods to solve number problems, clearly communicating my processes and solutions.
- +/-/x/÷: Recall number facts quickly and use them accurately when making calculations.
- Time: Work out how long a journey will take, the speed travelled at or distance covered, using knowledge of link between time, speed and distance.
- Measurement: Solve practical problems by applying knowledge of measure.

Wales (Key Stage 3)
- Skills: Select and use the mathematics, units of measure, sequences of operation and methods of computation to solve problems.
- Skills: Break complex problems into a series of tasks.
- Skills: Use a range of mental, written and calculator computational strategies.
- Skills: Interpret mathematical information presented in a variety of forms.
- Measures and money: Make estimates of time in everyday situations, extending to less familiar contexts.

Materials

several wooden cylinders, blocks such as base 10 hundred, calculator

Focus

This page explores the use of models in coming to terms with problem situations and analysing the possibilities that make up the whole solution. Logical reasoning, as well as an understanding of the circumference concept, is required. Diagrams are also helpful to organise and explore the data.

Discussion

Page 61
It will be helpful for pupils to first model the action of the obelisk moving along with the aid of rollers. If a block is set up on two or more cylinders touching each other and the point of contact of the block and the front cylinder are marked, it will be possible to see how the block moves forward on the cylinders at the same time as the cylinders move along the ground. For each complete turn of the rollers, the obelisk must move a distance equal to the circumference along the rollers and a further distance equal to the circumference along the ground.

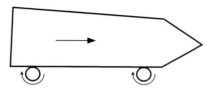

Since the circumference of a roller is 6.25 m, the obelisk will move forward 12.5 m with each rotation of the rollers. To move 3.2 km or 3200 m requires 3200 ÷ 12.5 or 256 rotations. Each day the obelisk moves 12 rotations or 150 m. After 21 days it would have moved 3150 m, after 22 days it would have moved 3300 m. The obelisk would have moved 3200 m on the 22nd day after Friday—a Saturday.

The experience with the rollers will help in imagining how the gears move—Gear B would move in a clockwise direction, Gear C in an anticlockwise direction. Gear C has 3 x 48 teeth, so Gear B would make 6 turns and Gear A would make 4 turns to engage this many teeth.

When Gear A rotates 12 times to lower 216 m, 12 x 36 teeth would need to engage. Gear C would need to rotate 9 times to lower the load (9 x 48 teeth would need to engage).

Possible difficulties

- Unable to see how the obelisk will move a distance along the rollers and also a distance along the ground
- Not seeing that division is required to find the number of times the rollers rotate
- Not realising that the obelisk would not require a whole number of days to reach the Nile and would be there during the 22nd day
- Unable to see how 22 days is 3 weeks and 1 day hence it must be 1 day after a Friday, or a Saturday, that it reached the Nile

Extension

- Ask how far the obelisk will have travelled after 5, 10 or 15 days.
- Pose similar problems to the one on the page where large granite blocks are moved on rollers with different circumferences, and different distances to reach the Pyramids and other large Egyptian constructions.
- If pupils are familiar with calculating circumferences using the ratio π, pose similar problems where the radius of the roller is given.
- Change the number of teeth on each of the gear wheels (they need to have factors in common to work).
- Have pupils investigate the use of rollers, block and tackles and gear levers in other situations; e.g. on cranes, boats, winches.

1. (a) The ancient Egyptians made their obelisks by cutting and shaping large granite pieces from a quarry near Aswan. Log rollers were used to move them to the Nile River so they could be floated to where they were needed at Luxor. If the circumference of each roller was 6.25 m, how far did the obelisk stone move for each complete turn of the rollers?

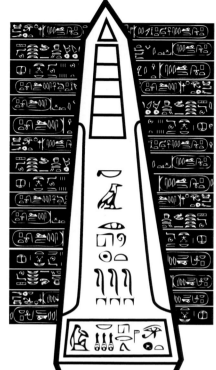

_____

_____

   (b) How many times would the rollers have to rotate to move the obelisk the 3.2 km to the Nile River?

_____

   (c) The workers were able to turn each roller through 12 rotations per day. If they started moving the obelisk on a Friday, on which day did it reach the Nile River?

_____

_____

2. In the time of the ancient Egyptians, a pulley was used to lift relatively small objects as it is easier to pull down on a rope than to lift up with a rope. These days, systems of pulleys or geared wheels are used on cranes that lift and lower large objects so they can be swung into position rather than rolled into place.

   In this system, Gear A has 36 teeth, Gear B has 24 teeth and Gear C has 48 teeth.

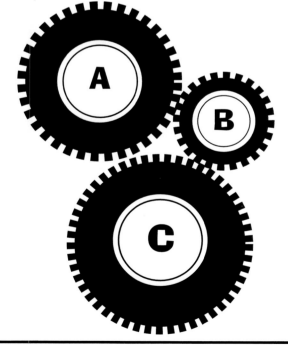

   (a) When Gear A turns in an anticlockwise direction, in which direction do Gears B and C turn?

_____

_____

   (b) When Gear C makes 3 complete turns, how many turns do Gears B and A make?

_____

_____

   (c) If each rotation of Gear A lowers a heavy load 18 m, how many times would Gear C need to rotate to lower the load 216 m?

_____

Note: Many solutions are written statements rather than just numbers. This is to encourage teachers and pupils to solve problems in this way.

SURFACE AREA .... page 3

1. Steps are 0.4 m², rises are 0.2 m², ends are 0.02 m²
    Area painted = 3.1 m²
2. 6.1 m²
3. 78 cm²
4. Yes – 72 cm²
5. (a) 132 cm²
    (b) Hole would be 2 x 2 x 2 – surface area would be
         108 cm²
6. 1 cube removed – 186 cm²
    9 cubes removed – 222 cm²
7. Surface 1 cube, hole 1 cube – 180 cm²
    Surface 9 cubes, hole 1 cube – 216 cm²
    Surface 9 cubes, hole 9 cubes – 168 cm²

VOLUME AND SURFACE AREA .... page 4

1. (a) 1 layer inside the prism
    (b) A smaller prism 3 x 5 x 7 (the prime factors of 105)
    (c) Whole prism is 5 x 7 x 9
         315 cm³
    (d) 2 of each side: 5 x 7, 5 x 9, 7 x 9
         286 cm²
2. 363=3 x 11 x 11, so
    Whole prism is 5 x 13 x 13
    Volume is 845 cm³
    Surface area is 598 cm²
3. (a) 60 = 2 x 2 x 3 x 5
         Prism could be
         4 x 3 x 5,
         2 x 6 x 5,
         2 x 2 x 15,
         or 2 x 3 x 10.
    (b)

Internal prism	Volume of prism	Surface area of prism
4 x 3 x 5	210 x 8 = 1680 cm³	856 cm²
2 x 6 x 5	1792 cm³	928 cm²
2 x 2 x 15	2176 cm³	1152 cm²
2 x 3 x 10	1920 cm³	1056 cm²

SURFACE AREA AND VOLUME .... page 5

1. (a) 600 cm²
    (b) 792 cm³
    (c) Surface area 680 cm² Volume 992 cm³
         (25 more blocks – equivalent to 1 more layer extra
         volume is 200 cm³, extra area is 80 cm²)
2. (a) Volume 1458 cm³ Surface area 981 cm²
    (b) (i) Volume 360 cm³ Surface area 416 cm²
         (ii) Volume 1215 cm³ Surface area 900 cm²
         (iii) Volume 3584 cm³ Surface area 1792 cm²

THE FARMERS MARKET .... page 7

1. Use 'Try and adjust' by choosing a likely number, then 25
    less than half of it:

	Saturday	Sunday	total sold
Try	300	125	425 – too few
Try	400	175	575 – too many
Try	390	170	560 – too few
Try	398	174	572

He sold 398 avocados on Saturday, 174 avocados on
Sunday

2.

Sandwich stall	Lance	third customer	Lance	next customer	Lance	first customer	Lance
55							
	55	56					
			111	112			
					223	224	
							447

He had 447 tomatoes at the start of the market.

3.

fourth customer	Lance	third customer	Lance	next customer	Lance	first customer	Lance
3							
	3	9					
			12	18			
					30	36	
							66

He brought 66 pumpkins to the market.

PROFIT AND LOSS .... page 9

1.

Items sold per week	50	75	100	250	500	1000	1500	3000
Income	2500	3750	5000	12 500	25 000	50 000	75 000	150 000
Total costs	4000 + 750	4000 + 115	4000 + 1500	4000 + 3750	4000 + 7500	4000 + 15 000	4 000 + 22 500	4000 + 45 000

2. Loss
3. Profit
4. Between 100 and 250

	110	113	114	115
Income	5500	5650	5700	5750
Costs	4000	4000	4000	4000
	1650	1695	1710	1725
	5650	5695	5710	5725

115 items

CALCULATOR PATTERNS .... page 10

1. (a) 4899
    (b) 4900
    (c) difference of 1
    (d) Numbers will vary but difference will always be 1
    (e) Numbers will vary but difference will always be 1

Note: Many solutions are written statements rather than just numbers. This is to encourage teachers and pupils to solve problems in this way.

(f) For consecutive numbers, the product of the number before and the number after is 1 less than the number squared, number^2.

The number before is (number − 1),
the number after is (number + 1)

(number − 1) x (number +1)

= number x number + number x 1
  − 1 x number − 1 x 1

= number^2 + number − number − 1

= number^2 − 1

No matter what number is chosen, there will always be a difference of 1

2. (a) 279

(b) 93

(c) 3

(d) e.g. 47
difference between 4^3 and 7^3 is 279
$4^2 + (4 \times 7) + 7^2 = 93$
$279 \div 93 = 3$
Try 83
difference between 8^3 and 3^3 is 485
$8^2 + (8 \times 3) + 3^2 = 97$
$485 \div 97 = 5$

(e) answer is always the difference between the tens and ones digits

(f) e.g. 346 is 34 and 6 or 3 and 46
Difference is 28 or 43

(g) Pattern
when a 3 digit number is split into two parts, the difference of the cubes of the parts divided by the sum of the squares and the product of the two parts is the same as the difference between the two parts.
This result is a consequence of the algebraic relationship
$a^3 − b^3 = (a − b) \times (a^2 + ab + b^2)$. Showing pupils and asking them to substitute numbers for a and b will show pupils it always works – this is the what the questions have asked them to do in words.
Some pupils may be able to multiply out the brackets part by part in a similar way to the example above:

$(a − b) \times (a^2 + ab + b^2)$

= $(a \times a^2) + (a \times ab) + (a \times b^2) − (b \times a^2)$
  $− (b \times ab) − (b \times b^2)$

= $a3 + a^2b + ab^2 − a^2b − ab^2 − b^3$

= $a^3 − b^3$

PUZZLE SCROLLS .... page 11

1. £6.50
2. 169
3. 21
4. 27
5. 25
6. £268 and £232

WEATHER OR NOT.. page 13

1. Canberra and Brisbane
2. $\frac{27}{73}$ or 37%
3. Adelaide (42.2 + 1.3 = 43.5. Divide by 2 − 21.75°)
4. $\frac{47}{73}$ or 64%
5. Canberra
6. Brisbane, Sydney, Darwin
7. $\frac{28}{73}$ or 38%
8. Sydney, Darwin, Perth
9. $\frac{45}{73}$ or 62%
10. Adelaide

SHOWTIME .... page 14

1. $\frac{4}{10}$ or $\frac{2}{5}$
2. $\frac{1}{10}$
3. $\frac{1}{10}$
4. $\frac{2}{7}$
5. $\frac{2}{7} \times \frac{2}{7} \times \frac{2}{7} \times \frac{2}{7}$ or $\frac{16}{2401}$
6. $\frac{1}{3}$
7. 1 in 19 683 or 1 in about 20 000
8. In terms of probability, no. Discussion should centre around the actual likelihood of customers buying 1 or more hot dogs.

PROBABLY TRUE .... page 15

1. Absolutely certain means a probability of 1.
40 cards must be drawn.
2. Probability of blue from bag 1 is $\frac{3}{5}$.
Probability of blue from bag 2 is $\frac{2}{3}$.
3. $\frac{15}{100}$ or $\frac{3}{20}$
4. Probability of drawing blue or yellow must be $\frac{1}{4}$.
There are 9 blue and yellow marbles so must be 36 altogether. 27 must be red. Need 24 more red marbles.
5. Probability for Carly is $\frac{4}{9}$, for Toby is $\frac{3}{8}$.
6. $\frac{8}{20}$ or $\frac{2}{5}$
7. $\frac{4}{16}$ or $\frac{1}{4}$

SOLUTIONS

Note: Many solutions are written statements rather than just numbers. This is to encourage teachers and pupils to solve problems in this way.

WILDERNESS EXPLORER .... page 17

1. CA47, CA51, CA68, TA51, TA68
2. CA23, CA32, TA23, TA32, TA47
3. CA74, TA74
4. CA47 at 7:10
   leave hotel at 7:10, arrive 7:45, plane at 8:45 arrive 10:20, check in 13:20, 14:20, 15:20 …
   CA51 at 10:00
   leave hotel at 10:00, arrive 10:35, plane at 11:35 arrive 13:10, check in 16:20, 17:20, 18:20
   CA68 at 12:50
   leave hotel at 12:50, arrive 13:25, plane at 14:25 arrive 16:00, check in 18:20
   TA51 at 9:05
   leave hotel at 9:05, arrive 9:40, plane at 10:40 arrive 12:15, check in 14:20, 15:20, 16:20
   TA68 at 12:45
   leave hotel at 12:45, arrive 13:10, plane at 14:10 arrive 15:45, check in 18:20
5. Discussion needs to consider time needed to get to the campsite if the flight or luggage delayed.

CHANGING LOCKERS .... page 19

1. (a) Answers will vary.
   Colour squares or place counters on a grid to show when a door is open:

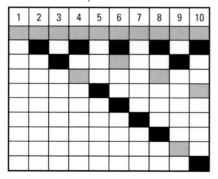

   A door is changed an odd number of times to remain open. These locker numbers are square numbers (one number as a factor twice, so an odd number of factors): 1, 4, 9, 16, 25, 49, ...
   A prime number has only two factors and these lockers will always be closed.

   (b) 1, 4, 9
   (c) 1, 4, 9, 16, 25, 49
   (d) Square numbers have an odd number of factors and these lockers will be open.
   (e) 1, 4, 9, 16, 25, 36, 49, 64, 81, 100, 121, 144, 169, 196, 225, 256, 289, 324, 361, 400, 441, 484, 529, 576, 625, 676, 729, 784, 841, 900, 961
   (f) 2, 3, 5, 7, 11, 13

(g) They are prime numbers and have only 2 factors
(h) The Sieve of Eratosthenes shows that after 2 and 3, all primes must be 1 more or less than a multiple of 6 (although some of these numbers are not prime – this was discussed in Book F).

1	**2**	**3**	4	**5**	6	**7**
8	9	10	**11**	12	**13**	
14	15	16	**17**	18	**19**	
20	21	22	**23**	24	25	
26	27	28	**29**	30	**31**	
32	33	34				

= 166 x 6 = 996 is the closest multiple of 6 to 1000, so 997 is the largest prime.
997 is the largest locker number that is only changed twice.

CYCLE DAYS .... page 20

1. Looking at their rates of walking and cycling, in 15 minutes Jane walks 1 km and Jenny cycles 3 km:

Jane walking

minutes	distance walked	distance left to cycle	time taken
15	1	15	1 hour 45 minutes
30	2	14	1 hour 54 minutes
45	3	13	2 hours 3 minutes
60	4	12	2 hours 12 minutes
75	5	11	2 hours 21 minutes
90	6	10	2 hours 30 minutes

Jenny cycling

minutes	distance cycled	distance left to walk	time taken
15	3	13	2 hours 51 minutes
30	6	10	2 hours 30 minutes
45	9	7	2 hours 90 minutes
60	12	4	1 hour 48 minutes

They can arrive home together after 2 hours 30 minutes. Jenny cycles for 30 minutes and walks the remaining 10 km in 2 hours. Jane walks for 90 minutes to reach the bicycle and cycles the remaining 10 km in 1 hour.

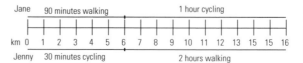

Jenny should ride her bicycle for 30 minutes

SOLUTIONS

Note: Many solutions are written statements rather than just numbers. This is to encourage teachers and pupils to solve problems in this way.

2. The slower speed requires an additional 10 km, the faster speed covers 15 km too much:

hours	distance @ 10km/hr	distance to park	distance @ 15 km/hr	distance to park
1	10	20	15	0
2	20	30	30	15
3	30	40	45	30
4	40	50	60	45
5	50	60	75	60

After 5 hours, the distance to the park at each speed is the same – 60 km.
She would arrive at the exact time cycling at 12 km per hour.

3. The slower speed requires an additional 8 km, the faster speed cover 12 km too much:

hours	distance @ 10km/hr	distance to park	distance @ 15 km/hr	distance to park
1	10	20	15	0
2	20	30	30	15
3	30	40	45	30
4	40	50	60	45
5	50	60	75	60

After 5 hours, the distance to the park at each speed is the same – 48 km.
She would arrive at the exact time cycling at 9.6 km per hour

4. Both Jenny and Jane should leave at 7:00 am

PUZZLE SCROLLS .... page 21

1. £7000
2. width 6 m, length 12 m
3. 210 blocks
4. 7 @ 60p, 8 @ 85p
5. 57 times. Pupil answers will vary and it is unlikely they will find them all.
6. 32 cm

OFFICE HOURS... page 23

1.

Time	5:00	5:01	5:02	5:03	5:04	5:05	5:06	5:07	5:08	5:09	5:10
Sally	6	5	5	5	5	4	3	3	3	3	2
Cath	6		5		4	4	4	4		3	

Time	5:11	5:12	5:13	5:14	5:15	5:16
Sally	2	2	2	2	1	
Cath	2		1			

(a) Cath
(b) Cath 13 minutes, Sally 15 minutes

2.

Time	5:00	5:01	5:02	5:03	5:04	5:05	5:06	5:07	5:08	5:09	5:10
Sally	8	7	7	7	7	6	5	5	5	5	4
Cath	8		7		6	6	6	6		5	

Time	5:11	5:12	5:13	5:14	5:15	5:16	5:17	5:18	5:19	5:20
Sally	4	4	4	3	2	2	2	2	1	
Cath	4		3	3	3	3		2		1

(a) No: fast lift takes 19 minutes, slow lift takes 20 minutes
(b) The slow lift takes 22 minutes, the fast life takes 23 minutes

Time	5:00	5:01	5:02	5:03	5:04	5:05	5:06	5:07	5:08	5:09	5:10
Sally	9	8	8	8	8	7	6	6	6	6	5
Cath	9		8		7	7	7	7		6	

Time	5:11	5:12	5:13	5:14	5:15	5:16	5:17	5:18	5:19	5:20	5:21
Sally	5	5	5	4	3	3	3	3	2	2	2
Cath	5		4	4	4	4		3		2	

Time	5:22	5:23
Sally	2	1
Cath	1	

3. 25 people

AT THE OFFICE... page 24

hours	240/hr	280/hr	difference (copies)
10	2400	2800	400
20	4800	5600	800
15	3600	4200	600

1. (a) 4000
   (b) 15 hours
2. (a) 20 minutes
   (b) 15 minutes
3. (a) 2400

number	60/hr	75/hr	difference (hours)
300	5	4	1
600	10	8	2
1200	20	16	3
2400	40	32	8

(b) 35 hours

SOLUTIONS

Note: Many solutions are written statements rather than just numbers. This is to encourage teachers and pupils to solve problems in this way.

OUT OF OFFICE .... page 25

1.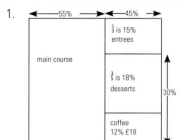

   1% is £1.50. The boss paid £150

2.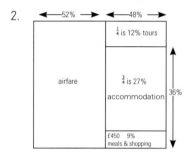

   (a) Accommodation cost £1350. 1% is £50.
   (b) Airfare cost £2600.

3.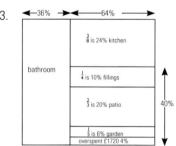

   1% is £430.
   Renovating the kitchen cost £15 480, the bathroom cost £10 320, the patio cost £8600.

NUMBER PATTERNS .... page 27

1. (b) Yes
   (c) Get a square number
   (d)
   (e) $T_2 + T_3 = S_3$
       $T_3 + T_4 = S_4$, etc
2. (b) Third diagonal
   (c) diagonally below last number

MAGIC SQUARES .... page 29

114

21	18	**15**	30
16	**29**	22	17
28	13	**20**	23
19	**24**	27	**14**

24	21	**18**	32
19	31	**25**	**20**
30	**16**	23	26
22	**27**	29	**17**

59	56	53	66
54	**65**	60	55
64	51	58	**61**
57	**62**	63	**52**

42	39	**36**	49
37	48	**43**	38
47	**34**	41	44
40	**45**	46	35

20	**17**	14	**28**
15	27	**21**	16
26	**12**	19	22
18	23	**25**	13

89	86	**83**	98
84	97	90	**85**
96	81	**88**	91
87	92	95	**82**

24	21	**18**	**32**
19	31	25	20
30	**16**	23	**26**
22	27	**29**	17

72	**69**	66	82
67	81	**73**	68
80	**64**	71	**74**
70	**75**	**79**	65

22	**19**	16	**29**
17	28	**23**	18
27	14	21	24
20	**25**	26	15

SUDOKU .... page 30

5	7	2	1	9	4	8	3	6
8	3	1	7	6	2	5	9	4
4	9	6	5	3	8	7	2	1
9	1	8	6	2	5	3	4	7
7	6	5	8	4	3	9	1	2
3	2	4	9	1	7	6	8	5
1	4	9	3	5	6	2	7	8
6	8	3	2	7	1	4	5	9
2	5	7	4	8	9	1	6	3

8	9	7	5	4	1	2	3	6
6	1	4	3	7	2	8	5	9
3	5	2	9	8	6	4	1	7
1	6	8	4	2	3	7	9	5
5	4	3	7	6	9	1	2	8
2	7	9	1	5	8	6	4	3
4	2	5	8	3	7	9	6	1
9	8	6	2	1	5	3	7	4
7	3	1	6	9	4	5	8	2

4	8	7	9	5	2	3	1	6
6	1	9	4	3	8	2	7	5
3	5	2	7	1	6	9	8	4
9	4	5	1	2	7	6	3	8
1	7	8	3	6	4	5	9	2
2	6	3	8	9	5	7	4	1
7	2	4	5	8	3	1	6	9
5	3	1	6	4	9	8	2	7
8	9	6	2	7	1	4	5	3

3	6	5	7	1	4	2	8	9
2	8	1	6	5	9	7	3	4
9	7	4	3	8	2	6	5	1
8	1	3	5	2	6	9	4	7
5	2	6	9	4	7	8	1	3
4	9	7	1	3	8	5	6	2
6	4	9	8	7	1	3	2	5
1	5	8	2	9	3	4	7	6
7	3	2	4	6	5	1	9	8

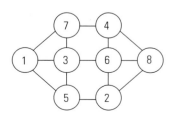

SOLUTIONS

Note: Many solutions are written statements rather than just numbers. This is to encourage teachers and pupils to solve problems in this way.

ALPHAMETIC PUZZLES .... page 31

Examples of solutions are:

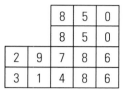

AT THE SHOPS .... page 33

1. I paid £179.90
2. 3 DVDs £36
   2 CDs £37.50
3. (a) Total: £1348.20
   (b) £960 is 80% of the cost.
       20% is £240.
       Cost is £1200
4. (a) 2 jeans and 3 t-shirts
   (b) £247.50
5. £69 for the first pair, £34.50 for the second pair

80% is £960	20% off

THE PLANT NURSERY .... page 34

1. 32 292 seedlings
2. 2808 seedlings
3. £15 276 profit
4. 1212 seedlings
5. One way to explore 324 seedlings planted in punnets of 4 and 9 is to look at multiples. Thinking about combinations of multiples of 9 and 4 which add to 324 soon shows a pattern. Key 324 into a calculator, subtract 9 and hit the equal key over and over to continue to subtract 9. This gives numbers which add to 324 with a multiple of 9. Check which numbers are multiples of 4 (a number is divisible by 4 if the last two digit are divisible by 4). The first number divisible by 4 is 288. Keep hitting the equal key and record the numbers which are divisible by 4.

Display on calculators	Take away 9	Multiple of 4 (punnets)	Add to 324 (punnets)
315		288 (72)	36 (4)
306		252 (63)	72 (8)
297		216 (54)	108 (12)
288		180 (45)	144 (16)
		144 (36)	180 (20)

A pattern emerges and the table can be completed with out needing to continue with the calculator.
This give us the number of seedlings not the number of punnets and so each combination needs to be converted to punnets which is shown in the brackets.
72 and 4, 63 and 8, 54 and 12, 45 and 16, 36 and 20, 27 and 24, 18 and 28, 9 and 32

6. 55 punnets
7. Again multiples can be used to explore solutions to this investigation.
   The first table has 180 seedlings in 30 punnets. The second table has 167 seedlings in 34 punnets. Key 180 into a calculator, subtract 8 and hit the equal key, looking for multiples of 3 (a number is divisible by 3 when the sum of all the digits is divisible by 3). Only the numbers which are divisible by 3 need to be recorded.

Display on calculators	Take away 8	Multiple of 3 (punnets)	Multiples of 8 which add to 180 (punnets)
172		156	24
164		132	48
156		108	72
148		84 (28)	96 (12)
		60 (20)	120 (15)
The emerging pattern can be used to complete the table.		36 (12)	144 (18)
		12 (4)	168 (21)

This investigation however has the added criteria of 30 punnets and only one possibility adds to 30 punnets.
12 punnets of 3 and 18 punnets of 8 on the first table. Similar reasoning can be used for the second table. This list below shows there is only one possibility which adds to 34 punnets.

Multiple of 3 (punnets)	Multiples of 8 which add to 167 (punnets)
159	8
143	24
135	32
111 (37)	56
87 (29)	80 (10)
63 (21)	104 (13)
39 (13)	128 (16)
15 (5)	152 (19)

21 punnets of 3 and 16 punnets of 8 on the second table.

SOLUTIONS

Note: Many solutions are written statements rather than just numbers. This is to encourage teachers and pupils to solve problems in this way.

ON THE FARM .... **page 35**

1. 26 kg
2. 134.4 tonnes
3. 35% of the land i.e. 4.2 hectares
4. £0.28
5. 1 third of 1450 is 483.3 – 484 plants
   3% of 1450 is 43.5 – 44 plants
   He needs about 527 plants
6. Apples: 5.25 hectares, Peaches: 3.75 hectares
   Apricots: 1.8 hectares, Nectarines: 4.2 hectares
7. 494 truck loads are needed
   3 trucks make 124 trips and 1 makes 122 trips or 2 trucks
   make 124 trips and 2 make 123 trips

FISHERMAN'S WHARF .... **page 37**

1. The cost of the crabs and fish is £192 and the cost of the
   fish and crayfish is £135. Use a table to 'try and adjust'
   an amount for the crayfish:

	Crabs	Fish	Crayfish	Crabs & Fish	Fish & Crayfish	Crabs & Crayfish
Try	142	50	85	192	135	227 – too little
Try	150	42	93	192	135	243 – too little
Try	155	37	98	192	135	253 – too much
Try	160	32	103	192	135	263

   5 crabs cost £160, £32 each. Fish cost £32. 2 crayfish
   cost £103, £51.50 each.
   Chris's seafood cost £295.

2. (a) Use a table to 'try and adjust' an amount for each
       seafood:

	Whiting	Mussels	Scallops	whiting & mussels	mussels & scallops	whiting & scallops
Try	50	35	186.25	85	221.25	236.25 – too little
Try	55	30	191.25	85	221.25	246.25 – too little
Try	60	25	196.25	85	221.25	256.25 – too much
Try	57	28	193.25	85	221.25	250.25 – too much
Try	56	29	192.25	85	221.25	248.25 – too little
Try	56.25	28.75	192.50			248.75

   Whiting £56.25. Half-shell mussels £28.75.
   Scallops £192.50.
   (b) Mussels cost £5.75 per kg.
   (c) 1 kg of scallops costs £27.50
3. Coral trout £36, Reef cod £24
4. The head same as tail and ½ body.
   The body costs the same as the head and tail, so, the
   head costs same as the tail and ½ (head and tail) i.e. the
   head costs the same as ½ head and 1½ tails.
   The head must cost the same as 3 tails or £12, the body
   costs £16 and the fish costs £32.

MAKING DESIGNS .... **page 39**

1. (a) 10 cm
   (b) 100 cm²
   (c) 1100 cm²
   (d) 1600 cm² – 1100 cm² = 500 cm²
2. (a) 2500 cm²
   (b) 900 cm²
   (c) 0.36 or 36%
   (d) 0.44 or 44%
   (e) 0.2 or 20%
   (f) 50 cm²

SQUARES AND RECTANGLES .... **page 40**

1. Draw 3 lines from the other sides of the
   square to make 16 small squares.
   Each rectangle can now be seen as 4
   small squares.
   The perimeter of the rectangle, 15 cm, is the same as 10
   sides of the small squares.
   The side of the small square is 1.5 cm.
   The perimeter of the large square is 24 cm, the area is 36
   cm².
2. Draw 2 lines from the other sides of the
   square to make 9 small squares.
   Each rectangle can now be seen as 3
   small squares.
   The area of the rectangle is 192 cm², the area of each
   small square is 64 cm².
   The side of the small square is 8 cm.
   The perimeter of the large square is 96 cm, the perimeter
   of each rectangle is 64 cm.
3. Draw 4 lines from the other sides of the
   square to make 25 small squares.
   Each rectangle can now be seen as 5
   small squares.
   The area of the small square is 1.96 cm²
   The side of the small square is 1.4 cm.
   The perimeter of the rectangle is the same as 12 sides of
   the small square, 16.8 cm.
4. (a) 49 m   (b) 14
5. 31.5 m

DESIGNER SQUARES .... **page 41**

1.

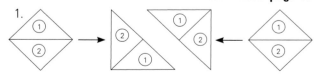

   A square with a side of 12 m and an area of 144 m²
   The area of each triangle is 36 m²
   The area of the diamond is 72 m²

Note: Many solutions are written statements rather than just numbers. This is to encourage teachers and pupils to solve problems in this way.

2. (a) The problem asks for a square number.
Checking systematically using a calculator shows:

square	square + 99	square + 200
...		
$15^2 = 225$	$18^2 = 324$	425 – not a square
...		
$23^2 = 529$	628 – not a square	$27^2 = 729$
...		
$49^2 = 2401$	$50^2 = 2500$	$51^2 = 2601$

(a) smallest square needs 2401 tiles
medium square needs 2500 tiles
largest square needs 2601 tiles

(b) 7502 yellow tiles

HOW MANY? .... page 43

1. 90 500 visitors
2. 203 125 visitors
3. 230 930 visitors

HOW FAR? .... page 44

1. 12 km per week
2. 1105 km
3. He swims 2880 m per day – about 20 km per week
4. 375 km
5. Each week she swims 12 km, runs 14 km and bikes 19 km. Assuming 4 weeks in a month.
She swims 48 km, runs 56 km and bikes 76 km per month.

HOW MUCH? .... page 45

1. £560
2. £327.75 Payment per seedling is better than £273.75 by £54
3. 120
4. £84.75 for shelving without brackets and screws is cheaper than £97.50 for shelving with brackets and screws by £12.75
5. £816

PROSPECT PLAINS... page 47

1. (a) There are 50 eggs to collect:

Egg collected	Distance run	Total distance (metres)
1 & 2	4	4
3 & 4	8	4 + 8
5 & 6	12	4 + 8 + 12
7 & 8	16	4 + 8 + 12 + 16
9 & 10	20	4 + 8 + 12 + 16 + 20

Look for a pattern
4
4(1 + 2)
4(1 + 2 + 3)
4(1 + 2 + 3 + 4)
4(1 + 2 + 3 + 4 + 5)

Egg collected	Distance run	Total distance (metres)
1 & 2	4	4

4(1 + 2 + 3 + 4 + 5 ... + 50)

This can be totalled on a calculator to give the answer of 5100 m or 5 km 100 m.
Another way is to look for a pattern:
4, 4(1 + 2), 4(1 + 2 + 3), 4(1 + 2 + 3 + 4), ...
Sum wanted is   1 + 2 + 3 + 4 + 5 ... + 50
This sum is also 50 + 49 + 48 + ... +   + 1
Adding these two expressions of the distance shows that twice the sum must be 50 x 51
The sum is half 50 x 51
4 x half (50 x 51) is 5100
The winner ran 5100 or 5 km 100 m

(b) The distance to run each egg halves, giving 2 + 4 + 6 + 8 + ...
The number of eggs remains, so the distance run would be 2 x half (25 x 26)
650 m – barely 1 eighth of the original

(c) Pick up eggs 3 at a time with a distance of 60 m.
Distance to run to the eggs and back to the basket:
6 + 12 + 18 + ... or 6 x (1 + 2 + 3 + ... + 20).
The total distance is 6 x half (20 x 21)
1200 m

MONEY MATTERS .... page 49

1.

Amount	£220		£200	£150
	Mother	Son	Mother + daughter	Son + daughter
Try	£120	£100	£80	£180 – too much
Try	£130	£90	£70	£160 – too much
Try	£140	£80	£60	£140 – too little
Try	£135	£85	£65	£150 – correct

Mother spent £135, son spent £85, daughter spent £65

2. (a) Brian got £76, Carol got £54
(b) Their aunt gave them £220

3.

Daughter £48 000, Grandson £30 000, Great grandchildren £5000 each

Note: Many solutions are written statements rather than just numbers. This is to encourage teachers and pupils to solve problems in this way.

SCORING POINTS .... page 50

1. (a) 8

correct	not correct/not answered	score
10	0	50
9	1	42
8	2	34
7	3	26

(b) 50, 42, 34, 26, 18, 10, 2

(c)

correct	incorrect	unanswered	score
20	0	0	60
19	0	1	57
	1	0	56
18	0	2	54
	1	1	53
	2	0	52
17	0	3	51
	1	2	50
	2	1	49
17	3	0	48
16	0	4	48
	1	3	47
	2	2	46
	3	1	45

17 correct and 0 unanswered,
16 correct and 4 unanswered.

(d) 3 questions were not answered correctly

incorrect	correct	prize
1	7	£1250
2	14	£2500
3	21	£3750

(e) Adding 1st + 2nd, 1st + 3rd, 2nd + 3rd gives
2(1st + 2nd + 3rd) = 194
97 people attended the first 3 shows, so 21 came to the 4th show

PUZZLE SCROLLS .... page 51

1. Rhyl
2. 6 minutes
3. 301 cows
4. 3946
5.
6. 91 cm²

Area of whole square is half 20² or 200 cm².
Area of square with diagonal 13² is half 13cm² or 84.5 cm².
Area of square with diagonal 7 is half 7² or 24.5 cm².
Area of shaded parts is 200 − 84.5 − 24.5 i.e. 91 cm².

RIDING TO WORK .... page 53

1.

Time	24 seconds	48 seconds	72 seconds	96 seconds	120 seconds	164 seconds	168 seconds	
Geoff	$\frac{3}{7}$	$\frac{6}{7}$	$\frac{9}{7}$	$\frac{12}{7}$	$\frac{15}{7}$	$\frac{18}{7}$	$\frac{21}{7}$	3 laps
Gary	$\frac{4}{7}$	$\frac{8}{7}$	$\frac{12}{7}$	$\frac{16}{7}$	$\frac{20}{7}$	$\frac{24}{7}$	$\frac{28}{7}$	4 laps

After 6 minutes – Gary 3600 m, Geoff 2400 m

2. 8 (including the beginning)

3.

Time in minutes	Gary	Geoff
1	600	400
2	1200 − start	800
3	1800	1200 − start
4	2400 − start	1600
5	3000	2000
6	3600 − start	2400 − start

(a) Gary cycles around the track in 42 seconds.
(b) After 2 minutes 48 seconds
(c) Geoff 3, Gary 4

4. 15 laps
5. (a) 3 minutes 30 seconds
   (b) 17 laps

BIKE TRACKS .... page 54

1.

Time	40 seconds	80	120	160	200	240	280	320	360	
Gina	$\frac{4}{9}$	$\frac{8}{9}$	$\frac{12}{9}$	$\frac{16}{9}$	$\frac{20}{9}$	$\frac{24}{9}$	$\frac{28}{9}$	$\frac{32}{9}$	$\frac{36}{9}$	4 laps
Georgia	$\frac{5}{9}$	$\frac{10}{9}$	$\frac{15}{9}$	$\frac{20}{9}$	$\frac{25}{9}$	$\frac{30}{9}$	$\frac{35}{9}$	$\frac{40}{9}$	$\frac{45}{9}$	5 laps

90 seconds

2. After 6 minutes
3. Gina 5, Georgia 4
4. 5 laps
5. 60 days later
6. 2 (including the first Saturday)
7. Saturday, Wednesday
8. Every 20 days
9. Every 12 days
10. Every 10 days

PUZZLE SCROLLS .... page 55

1. 70.89 m
2. 23 400
3.
4. 42 m
5. Jack £90, John £45
6. 111.5 m long 75.2 m wide

SOLUTIONS

Note: Many solutions are written statements rather than just numbers. This is to encourage teachers and pupils to solve problems in this way.

FARM WORK .... page 57

1. 6 days
2. 4 days
3. $1\frac{1}{5}$ days
4. 8 workers, 10 days
5. 12 minutes

FARM PRODUCE .... page 58

1. (a) At 17:00 an equal amount (192 m³) of water in each dam

   (b) 1176 m³

time	Dam 1 (48 m³)	Dam 2 (72 m³)
7:00	672	840
8:00	624	840
9:00	576	768
10:00	528	696
11:00	480	624
12:00	432	552
13:00	384	480
14:00	336	408
15:00	288	336
16:00	240	264
17:00	192	192

2. She had 400 fish to sell (and sold 380)

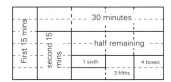

3. She sold 1400 fish in 56 boxes

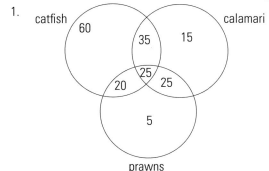

SELLING FISH .... page 59

1.

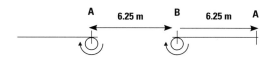

catfish — 60
calamari — 15
35
25
20   25
5
prawns

2. 125
3. 5
4. 140
5. 45

ROLLING ALONG .... page 61

1. (a) 12.5 m

   A ← 6.25 m → B ← 6.25 m → A

   If a roller is at point A on the obelisk before the turn and at point B after one complete turn, then the obelisk has moved the circumference of the roller or 6.25 m along the rollers.
   At the same time, the rollers have moved 6.25 m along the ground.
   So the obelisk moves 2 x 6.25 m or 12.5 m for each complete turn of the rollers.

   (b) 256
   To move 3.2 km or 3200 m requires
   3200 ÷ 12.5 or 256 rotations.

   (c) 150 m per day, so the 22nd day – a Saturday
   Each day the obelisk moves 12 rotations or 150 m.
   After 21 days it would have moved 3150 m, after 22 days it would have moved 3300 m.
   The obelisk would have moved 3200 m on the 22nd day after Friday – a Saturday

2. (a) Gear B – clockwise
   Gear C – anti-clockwise

   (b) Gear B – 6 rotations, Gear A – 4 rotations

   (c) 9 times
   Gear B would move in a clockwise direction, Gear C in an anti-clockwise direction.
   Gear C has 3 x 48 or 3 x 4 x 12 teeth.
   Gear B would make 6 turns to engage this many teeth (6 x 2 x 12 teeth).
   Gear A would make 4 turns to engage with many teeth (4 x 3 x 12 teeth).
   Gear A needs to rotate 12 times to lower 216 m (12 x 18 m).
   12 x 36 teeth would need to engage.
   Gear C would need to rotate 9 times to lower the load.
   (9 x 4 x 12 = 12 x 3 x 12)

ISOMETRIC RESOURCE PAGE

0–99 BOARD RESOURCE PAGE

0	1	2	3	4	5	6	7	8	9
10	11	12	13	14	15	16	17	18	19
20	21	22	23	24	25	26	27	28	29
30	31	32	33	34	35	36	37	38	39
40	41	42	43	44	45	46	47	48	49
50	51	52	53	54	55	56	57	58	59
60	61	62	63	64	65	66	67	68	69
70	71	72	73	74	75	76	77	78	79
80	81	82	83	84	85	86	87	88	89
90	91	92	93	94	95	96	97	98	99

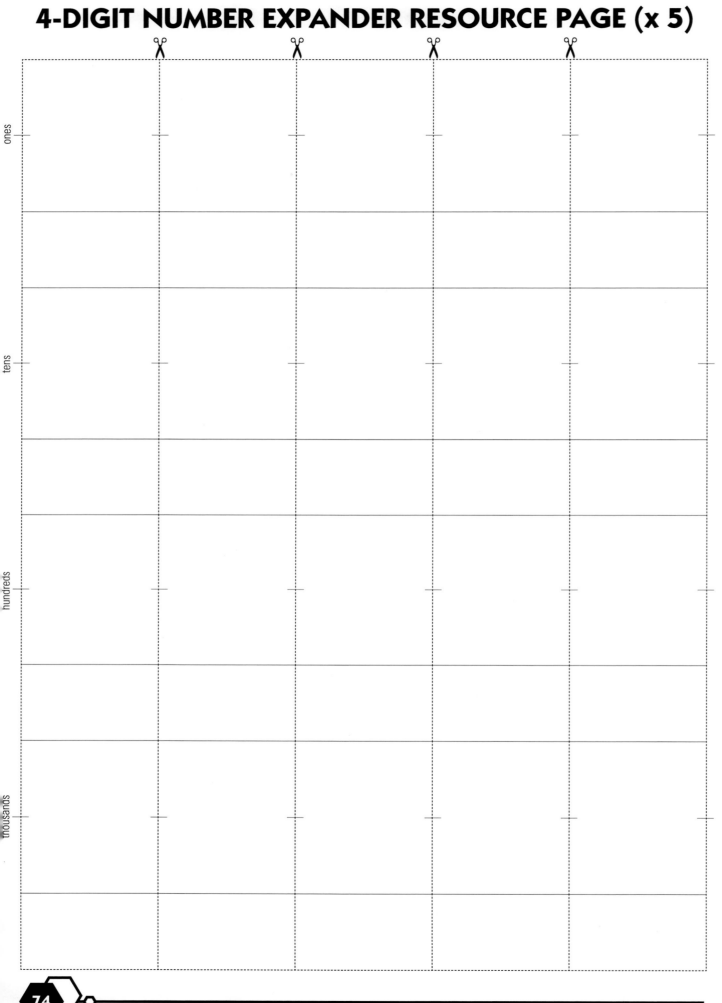

ones

tens

hundreds

thousands

10 mm x 10 mm GRID RESOURCE PAGE

15 mm x 15 mm GRID RESOURCE PAGE

TRIANGULAR GRID RESOURCE PAGE